Calder Hall

THE STORY OF BRITAIN'S
FIRST ATOMIC POWER STATION

by Kenneth Jay

*Atomic Energy Research Establishment
Harwell*

HARCOURT, BRACE & CO INC
NEW YORK

First published in 1956

Library of Congress Catalog Card Number: 56–11959

PRINTED IN GREAT BRITAIN

by Sir Edwin Plowden, K.C.B., K.B.E.

*Chairman of the United Kingdom Atomic
Energy Authority*

On 17 October 1956 when Her Majesty The Queen officially opens Calder Hall Nuclear Power Station, electric power will flow into the national electricity grid. This will be a memorable day in the history of the United Kingdom Atomic Energy Authority and a remarkable event for this country and for the whole world.

Industry depends on power. The revolutionary industrial developments of the last 200 years have been based primarily on the exploitation of coal as a source of power. To coal has been added—within little more than living memory—oil. In some parts of the world the force of flowing water has been used to generate electricity: but most of the world's power comes from the fossil fuels—coal and oil.

Now a new fuel and a new source of power is put to the service of mankind. The fuel is uranium and the source of power is 'atomic energy'. Calder Hall will be the first large-scale plant in the world to produce electricity by using the heat developed by the fission of uranium in nuclear reactors. It will demonstrate not on paper, not by a laboratory or pilot model, but on an industrial scale that scientists and engineers have found ways of adding to the world's store of wealth a new source of useful energy: a source with a potential large enough to allow the great industrial systems to continue hundreds—even thousands—of years beyond the time when the sources of power on which we have hitherto principally relied will have been exhausted.

This achievement would have been of particular importance to the United Kingdom even if the first station had not been a

British one. Coal was the foundation of our rise to industrial pre-eminence in the nineteenth century, but it is becoming increasingly hard to win in the ever greater quantities required by our continuing industrial development. Oil is being used more and more extensively, but this country itself is poor in oil resources. The geography of this small and densely-populated island is such that water power does not, and cannot be expected to, meet more than a small fraction of our needs of power. Great Britain, therefore, stood more in need of some new source of power than countries which are larger or less densely populated or which have vast resources of fossil fuel still to exploit.

The achievement is a British one, and this gives it an additional importance. It is a demonstration of what British skill can do and—over and above that—it has given the sort of incentive to advance in allied industrial fields that great technological achievements have always done. In the designing and building of Calder Hall the Atomic Energy Authority have made a wide variety of unusual and exacting demands upon industry—for materials of unusual purity, for equipment of unprecedented complexity, and so on. These demands, all of which have been met, will have their effects on fields far removed from the generation of nuclear power and give the stimulus that is required if a country is to continue, as this country must, among the industrial leaders of the world.

The process will continue. Calder Hall will be followed by more powerful and more advanced stations. At first these will be based on the same sort of reactor as there is at Calder Hall. Later other types of nuclear reactor will take their places in the country's nuclear power programme. That programme will go on expanding. Within ten to fifteen years we may have reached the point at which every new power station will be a nuclear power station. In the coming decades, therefore, the nuclear power industry will make an increasing contribution to, and provide a continuing stimulus for, the rest of British industry. The role of the Atomic Energy Authority in this will be to lead the way—to design, build and operate new types of reactor. As has already happened with Calder Hall, the lessons of the Authority's pioneering work will be passed on to enable industry to undertake the large-scale expansion that lies ahead.

Atomic energy is news. It has been through the whole of its short history. For this very reason there is a danger that the really significant development may not stand out as it should from the many interesting but minor ones which catch the public eye. In any true perspective the opening of Calder Hall must bulk large, particularly for this country. Ten years ago this country had no organization for studying or exploiting atomic energy in either its military or its civil applications. Throughout the ten years, moreover, there have been rival calls on the scientific and engineering manpower of the country and on our material resources to an extent never previously known in time of peace. In spite of all this the project which is now the Atomic Energy Authority has been built up until it numbers some 24,000 people. The men and women of the Authority, under the leadership of Sir John Cockcroft, Sir Christopher Hinton and Sir William Penney, and with the help of industry, have, besides all their contributions to national strength and scientific advance, been the first people anywhere to harness atomic energy on an industrial scale to the service of us all.

Contents

Plates

Plates

CHAPTER ONE

Power from the Atom: First Thoughts

In the autumn of 1956 atomic energy will for the first time contribute directly to Britain's sources of industrial power when the nuclear power station at Calder Hall, in Cumberland, begins to feed substantial amounts of electricity into the Central Electricity Authority's grid. The occasion will be a milestone in the industrial history not only of this country but also of the world. The USA and the USSR have previously demonstrated the possibilities of nuclear power by generating small quantities of electricity in experimental plants, and the USA has for some time had an operational submarine driven by atomic energy, but Great Britain's Calder Hall station will be the first to operate on a truly industrial scale. It is designed to generate some 90,000 kW of electrical power, and at the same time to manufacture plutonium, the artificial nuclear fuel, for military purposes.

This book is a report on Calder Hall. Its purpose is to describe the chain of thoughts and events which led to the design chosen for this station, the early gropings and flashes of inspiration, the systematic study on paper and in the laboratory of the feasibility of various proposals, the emergence of an engineering design, the construction with its concomitant development and research, and finally the possibilities for the future of this type of plant and its place in the Government's ten-year programme for industrial atomic energy. But before going into these details we shall first recapitulate the basic facts about the atom and the principles underlying atomic energy.

ATOMS AND NUCLEAR FUELS

An atom of matter is like an incredibly tiny solar system. It has a central sun, called the nucleus, round which move electrons, the planets of the system. The diameter of the nucleus is only about a ten-thousandth of that of the atom, yet in spite of its infinitesimally small size the nucleus is itself a complex body built up from particles called protons and neutrons, the ultimate building blocks of matter. Practically the whole mass of the atom is concentrated in the nucleus, for the mass of a planetary electron is less than a thousandth part of the mass of a proton or neutron.

When matter undergoes a chemical reaction, such as burning for example, the planetary electrons of its atoms are rearranged and as a consequence energy is released. This energy appears generally as heat, as the heat of a coal fire, or light, as in a gas flame. In these reactions the nuclei of the atoms taking part are undisturbed. In some circumstances, however, it is possible to produce a reaction in which a nucleus is disturbed or even broken up, and when this is done very much more energy may be released than is possible when only the planetary electrons are involved. Unlike chemical reactions nuclear reactions cannot generally be made to spread from one atom to the next; each nucleus has to be treated individually. But there is one exception to this rule, the reaction called nuclear fission, which is the cornerstone of nuclear power. Fission is produced when a nucleus of certain elements is struck by a neutron; the nucleus absorbs the neutron, its equilibrium is disturbed, and it is split into two more or less equal parts. In this splitting, energy is released and also more than one fresh neutron (actually about 2·5 neutrons per fission on the average); the latter are most important because they can cause further fissions in neighbouring atoms and these in their turn release more neutrons to cause yet another generation of fissions, and so on. In this way there is produced a self-sustaining chain reaction, a nuclear fire.

There are many fuels in which an ordinary fire can burn— coal, oil, gas, wood, even metals—but only one naturally occurring material will sustain a nuclear fire. That is the element uranium, a metal heavier than lead. Questions often asked by the layman at this point are: 'How do you light one of these nuclear fires? Do you have to switch on your reactor?' The answer is that the uranium is throwing off neutrons continuously, even before it is put into the reactor,

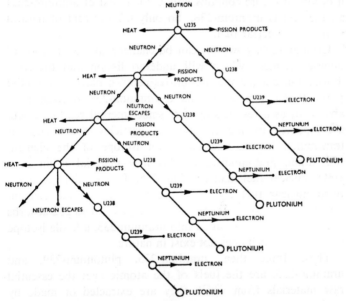

Figure 1. Nuclear fission in uranium-235.

but that the nuclear fire begins only when there is a sufficient quantity of uranium assembled in the favourable conditions of the reactor to sustain a chain reaction. This quantity is called the critical size. When the nuclear fire 'lights', the reactor is said to 'go critical' or 'become divergent'. A point to be remembered is that only a small fraction of the atoms in the uranium will 'burn', in the nuclear sense. Uranium consists of a mixture of two kinds of atoms, one of which is a little lighter than the other. These different atoms are called isotopes of uranium; they behave similarly in ordinary chemical reactions, but their nuclei differ in a way that leads to different behaviour when they are hit by neutrons. The lighter isotope, uranium-235, is easily split by neutrons of low energy but the heavier isotope, uranium-238, is not. Uranium-235 is in fact the part that burns, Now uranium as it occurs in nature contains only 0·7 per cent of uranium-235; all the rest is uranium-238. So only 0·7 per cent of natural uranium is nuclear fuel.

Uranium-238, however, can be changed into an isotope of another element which will undergo fission and therefore 'burn'. Once again the ubiquitous neutron plays an essential part. When a neutron hits a uranium-238 nucleus it is absorbed; as a result, and after some internal rearrangement accompanied by the emission of particles, the nucleus is transmuted into a nucleus of an isotope of the element plutonium, plutonium-239. This new material is an even better nuclear fuel than uranium-235. In a similar manner a third nuclear fuel can be made by exposing the element thorium to neutrons; the thorium isotope of mass 232 absorbs neutrons and is transmuted into uranium-233, a fissile isotope of uranium which does not exist in nature.

These three then, uranium-235, plutonium-239, and uranium-233, are the fuels of the atomic age; the essential raw materials from which they are extracted or made by nuclear transmutation are natural uranium and thorium. The striking thing about these nuclear fuels, compared with ordinary chemical fuels, is the enormous amount of energy that is released for each pound of fuel burnt. Thus a pound of uranium, if all the atoms in it were made to undergo fission, would release as much energy as 3,000,000 pounds (or 1,300 tons) of coal. Such complete utilization of uranium has yet to be realized in practice, though the fact that non-fissile uranium-238 can be transmuted into fissile plutonium implies that it is theoretically possible.

The energy released in fission is imparted in the first

instance to the two fragments into which the nucleus is split, causing them to move apart with great speed. No way of using the energy of these fragments directly has yet been devised but the motion through the uranium heats the metal and this heat can be removed and converted to mechanical energy by a steam engine or gas turbine (Figure 2). In short,

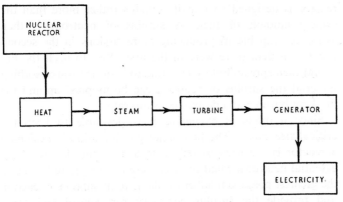

Figure 2. Stages in the generation of electricity by nuclear fission.

atomic energy is obtained by burning an uncommon fuel in an uncommon way and then using the heat obtained in a quite ordinary manner.

NUCLEAR REACTORS

The new fuels are burnt in new and different furnaces, called nuclear reactors or atomic piles. Because much of this book will be concerned with the design and construction of a particular type of nuclear reactor, these machines will be described in a little more detail. As has been said a nuclear fire is propagated by the neutrons released in fission, about 2·5 for each uranium atom split. Some of these neutrons may be lost, e.g. by being absorbed in materials other than fuel atoms or by escaping from the fuel, but provided enough of them remain to produce as many new fissions in the next generation as there were in the first, the chain reaction is maintained—the fire continues to burn at a constant rate. This state of affairs can be realized only if there is a certain minimum amount of fuel, the so-called critical size. With amounts less than the critical, so many neutrons escape that fewer fissions are produced in the second generation than occurred in the first, and the fire dies out. In practice a reactor is designed so that it contains rather more than the critical amount of fuel. A surplus of neutrons is then available, capable of producing more fissions in the second generation than there were in the first. Left to itself the fire would then spread, but by inserting rods of neutron-absorbing material the surplus of neutrons can be mopped up and the fire kept burning at a desired constant rate.

Since uranium is expensive it is desirable to keep the critical size small. The first major consideration in designing a reactor is the need to reduce to a minimum losses of the essential neutrons, whether by capture or escape, and so leave the greatest possible number available to maintain the reaction and provide the surplus necessary for control and other purposes.

A second major consideration in design is the energy of the neutrons producing fissions. Neutrons released in fission are moving at high speed; they are capable of producing more fissions at this speed, but the likelihood that they will do so is fairly small and consequently a reaction could be maintained only in highly concentrated nuclear fuel. On the other hand if the neutrons are slowed down the likelihood that they will produce fissions is greatly increased, although at the same time they are also more likely to be captured without producing fission. Nevertheless the balance is in favour of fission and a reaction can be maintained in less concentrated fuel. So there are two broad classes of reactors, fast-fission reactors in which the neutrons are used at high speed and thermal-fission reactors in which neutrons are slowed down to so-called thermal energies. This slowing-down is done by allowing the neutrons to bump about among the atoms of some light material, called a moderator; a neutron bounces off the light atoms and loses energy at each bounce, just as a snooker ball loses energy as it collides with one ball after another of the pool, until ultimately its energy is very small indeed. It should be noticed that the moderating action affects only the energy of the neutrons producing fission; it does not alter either the energy produced in fission or the power level at which the reactor operates.

For greatest efficiency, moderating materials must consist of light atoms; possible materials include the metal beryllium, the element carbon, and the element hydrogen or preferably its heavy isotope deuterium; hydrogen or deuterium are used in the form of water or heavy water respectively. The uranium fuel is then distributed throughout a large mass of the chosen moderator, the disposition being calculated to obtain the maximum slowing-down of neutrons followed by their utilization in fission, with the minimum loss by capture or escape. A typical thermal reactor is Bepo, the larger of the first two experimental reactors built at the Atomic Energy Research Establishment, Harwell. The principles of this reactor are illustrated in Figure 3. The moderator is carbon in the form of graphite. The reacting core consists of a cube built of graphite blocks so arranged as to leave horizontal channels running from side to side through the graphite; in these channels are placed rods of uranium enclosed in cans, made of a suitable light alloy, to protect them from corrosion and to prevent the escape of radioactive materials formed in fission. Operation of the reactor is controlled by pushing steel rods loaded with neutron-absorbing material (e.g. boron) into other channels in the core. To protect operators from the harmful effects of radiation released by radioactive materials, the core is built inside a thick concrete box which reduces the intensity of the radiations to a safe level.

The next important consideration in design is removal of the heat generated in the uranium rods. This is generally

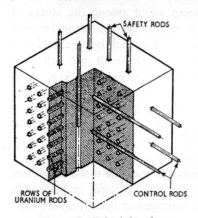

Figure 3. Principle of core arrangement in Bepo.

done by pumping some fluid through the channels; the fluid flows over the rods and carries off the heat. In Bepo the fluid is air, drawn at atmospheric pressure through the channels by powerful fans. The hot air is discharged up a 200-foot chimney and most of the heat is wasted. If the cooling air were compressed and pumped in a closed circuit over the uranium, the heat could be removed more efficiently; each cubic foot of compressed air could carry away more heat and the power required to pump the gas would be much reduced. Actually air is not a very good coolant even when compressed, but some other gases are quite efficient, certainly efficient enough to enable the heat to be used to generate power. As we shall see, compressed gas is used in the Calder Hall reactors. Still better coolants are liquids, such as water or certain liquid metals, and these will probably be used in some future reactors. Although more efficient than gases, liquids were not used in the first reactors for various reasons, some of which will be discussed later.

THE FIRST BRITISH REACTORS

The first nuclear reactors were built (in the USA) to manufacture plutonium for military purposes, but even in the midst of war scientists and engineers were thinking about using nuclear fission to generate industrial power. On the basis of the principles just outlined, there are hundreds of possible combinations that could be used in a reactor, fast reactors with different fuels and different methods of cooling,

1. Calder Hall: a general view.

2. The shell of a heat exchanger in position on its plinth.

thermal reactors with all the possible combinations of fuel and moderator and coolant, and so on. Many of these either would not be efficient or would be impracticable from an engineering standpoint, but there are perhaps fifteen or twenty practicable variants. Among them are gas-cooled piles of the type just described, and these were in fact considered during the war for plutonium production; they were, however, rejected in favour of reactors cooled by water. Towards the end of 1944 the British-Canadian research team at Montreal began to examine the design of reactors, for research purposes and for plutonium production, to be built in the United Kingdom. These workers had had no experience with reactors and had been denied access to much of the American information. They therefore concentrated their efforts largely upon types known to have worked in America, the slow-fission natural-uranium reactor, particularly the gas-cooled and water-cooled varieties.

At the end of 1945 the British Government set up an atomic energy project in the United Kingdom under the Ministry of Supply. It comprised the Atomic Energy Research Establishment (AERE) at Harwell and the Production Division with headquarters at Risley; the latter was to produce fissile material on a large scale. In August 1954, after an interim period of seven months under the Lord President of the Council, the two organizations were transferred to the United Kingdom Atomic Energy Authority; AERE is the Research Group of the Authority and the old production directorate is now called the Industrial Group of the Authority.[1]

The first task of the new department in 1945 was to build two research reactors for Harwell, the larger of the two, Bepo, being designed and built by the Industrial Group to Harwell specifications. Whilst Bepo was being built a much larger

[1] See the following publications by K. E. B. Jay:
Harwell: the British Atomic Energy Research Establishment, 1946–51, HMSO, 1952.
Britain's Atomic Factories: the Story of Atomic Energy Production in Britain, HMSO, 1954.
Atomic Energy Research at Harwell, Butterworth, 1955.

pile to produce plutonium on an industrial scale was being designed. For this it was decided to use natural uranium fuel and graphite moderator and originally it was intended to cool the pile with water, mainly because water had been used in American piles and was known to work well. It was, however, much more difficult to find a site suitable for a water-cooled pile in the crowded British Isles than in the United States. As a second string, therefore, the designers thought about gas cooling. At first sight they found this method unattractive. It looked as if the power needed to pump the gas through the reactor would be disproportionately large; it seemed also as if designing a satisfactory means for containing gas at high pressure would take too long. It should be noted that the designers were not then concerned with power generation but only to produce plutonium as soon as possible; they were therefore not interested in thermal efficiency but merely in getting rid of heat as cheaply as possible.

However, the picture was quite changed by a modification to the fuel elements, the uranium rods in their enclosing aluminium cans, which was suggested early in 1947 by Industrial Group engineers. Originally it had been intended to use simple cylindrical cans. The engineers now calculated that the pumping power needed to remove heat would be greatly reduced if the surface of the cans was extended by fitting fins along their length. This was no new idea but it had not hitherto been thought practicable in a reactor, because it was feared that the extra aluminium in the fins would absorb an excessive number of neutrons. Now it was shown that there need be no extra metal if the thickness of the can wall was reduced and the metal so saved put into the fins. and that the resulting can would still be strong enough for the duty required of it. The next step was taken at Harwell. The Risley workers' curves were extended to lower pressures and these curves showed that, if fins were used, a big reactor could be cooled by blowing air through it at atmospheric pressure without expending an extravagant amount of power in the blowers. Such a pile would not be as efficient as one cooled by gas under pressure, but it could be built more quickly and so plutonium production could begin earlier than seemed otherwise possible and the drawbacks of water-cooling would be avoided. On the basis of these calculations air-cooled reactors were built at Windscale for plutonium production.

EARLY IDEAS ABOUT POWER GENERATION

Although plutonium production had priority, the Risley engineers were keenly interested in power generation, and they proceeded to develop the application of finned cans from this point of view. They pointed out that fins, besides reducing pumping power, would have the further advantage that the gas would emerge from the reactor at a temperature not much lower than the temperature of the aluminium can itself—in short that fins would give hotter gas for a given maximum can temperature. And hotter gas meant the possibility of power generation. The point here is that, to generate power efficiently, high-pressure steam is needed; high pressure means high temperature in the steam and therefore in the source of heat (gas in this case) used to raise the steam. So the Risley engineers sketched the outlines of a reactor cooled by gas under pressure, which should be capable of turning heat into steam and thence electricity with an efficiency of 15 to 20 per cent. They discussed three gases as coolants, carbon dioxide, hydrogen, and helium (though most of the calculations were for carbon dioxide), and they suggested that the whole core should be enclosed in a steel shell capable of withstanding the pressure of the coolant gas. This idea was novel; up to that time proposals for gas-cooled reactors had assumed that the gas would be blown down separate tubes, one to each fuel channel. The new suggestion would greatly reduce the neutron-absorbing material in the core.

As we have said, all effort was at that time directed to producing plutonium quickly and new ideas were acceptable only so far as they contributed to that end. Finned cans in an air-cooled pile would lead to quicker plutonium production and were adopted; a pressure-resisting shell would take a long time to design and build, so it was rejected, and with it power generation. But the possibilities were too attractive to drop altogether and the ideas were studied at both Risley and Harwell, during 1947, in the hope that a reactor based on them might be built after the air-cooled piles were finished. In February 1948, industry was brought in for the first time when the Parolle Electrical Plant Co. Ltd were asked to study in more detail the steam side of a plant. For this purpose the reactor was defined simply as a box that generated a certain amount of heat and produced gas at a certain temperature and pressure; the problem was to find the most efficient way of using this heat. Parolle were joined by C. A. Parsons Ltd and Babcock and Wilcox Ltd, and from their joint work emerged a study that was later to be most valuable. At the time, however, the results could not be used. By the end of 1948 the urgency of the Industrial Group's defence commitments demanded that all engineering effort should be devoted to them and consequently study of power-generating reactors had to stop.

At Harwell in the meantime the attack on power generation went on. Many different ideas for reactors were put forward —someone once said that there was a new one every week— and discussed from every angle. Most of the work was theoretical but some experiments were made, among them detailed investigations into the heat transfer properties of different kinds of finned cans, primarily for the Windscale piles but giving results of great general value. In November 1949 a group of workers began, in collaboration with industry, a detailed study of a thermal reactor intended as a prototype power unit for a submarine. This reactor was to be cooled by helium gas and, in order to reduce the size, the fuel was to be slightly enriched in uranium-235. For various reasons the reactor was never built, but the very thorough study greatly clarified ideas about gas-cooled reactors. Valuable information relating to the cost of power generation became available from other sources also. Construction of the Windscale piles showed more closely what these machines were likely to cost to build. Canadian scientists at Chalk River provided for the first time facts about the period for which uranium fuel elements can be left in a reactor before the formation of neutron-absorbing fission products causes a serious loss of reactivity. From these last highly important data it was possible to obtain a realistic estimate of the proportion of uranium in a fuel element which could be burned, and hence of the fuel costs.

In September 1950 a conference was held at Harwell to review the possibilities of getting power from reactors fuelled with natural uranium, in the light of the more reliable information that was now forthcoming. Among the papers presented was one in which an engineer at Harwell gave new estimates of the cost of power generation from a gas-cooled reactor. The figure of less than a penny a unit was considerably lower than previous estimates and, although it provoked a great deal of discussion, was accepted as probably not far from the truth. Another important, though not new, idea was brought out strongly in this paper, viz. that a reactor of this type would, whilst generating power, produce plutonium that could later be used to fuel enriched reactors of more advanced design and so help to achieve better overall utilization of uranium, a concept that is fundamental to the current ten-year programme of nuclear power in the United Kingdom. Anxiety that the greatest proportion of uranium atoms should be burned was in fact the basis of most of the criticisms levelled at proposals for natural uranium reactors. In this type probably less than 1 per cent of the uranium could be burnt, whereas fast-fission reactors are capable of the process popularly called breeding, that is of producing by neutron-induced transmutation more of a secondary fuel (such as plutonium) than they burn of primary fuel (such as uranium) and so of utilizing a much higher fraction of the uranium.

In spite of the misgivings of the supporters of fast reactors, the conference as a whole agreed that there seemed every possibility that power generated by burning natural uranium would be no more costly than power derived from burning coal; at least the prospects were good enough to justify at once making technical studies and experiments aimed at building a plant in which operating experience could be obtained and costs realistically evaluated. Accordingly a team at Harwell was set up to see whether these early ideas could be converted into a feasible design. The work of this team, which began in January 1951 and led directly to Calder Hall, will be described in the next chapter.

CHAPTER TWO

The Design is Chosen: "Pippa"

A small group of engineers at Harwell were given instructions to investigate, with the help of specialists in the chemistry, metallurgy, and physics divisions, the feasibility of a nuclear plant for the simultaneous production of electric power and plutonium from natural uranium fuel. Natural uranium was in fact the only fixed condition in their discussions; all others had to be decided.

The group decided to tackle first the most difficult problem, the design of the reactor itself. When this began to look feasible, it would be time to consider steam-raising plant. The fixed point, natural uranium, meant that a thermal reactor would be essential. Starting from this, therefore, a careful and detailed survey was made of possible moderators and of possible coolants, gaseous and liquid.

BASIC DECISIONS

The possible moderators were beryllium (or beryllia), heavy water, and graphite. Beryllium is a light metal that does not absorb neutrons strongly; beryllia is its oxide. The disadvantage of these materials was that neither was likely to be available in quantity for a considerable time. Heavy water is water in which hydrogen (the H of the familiar H_2O formula) is replaced by deuterium, the hydrogen isotope of mass 2; it can be separated from ordinary water, of which it forms one part in six thousand, but the cost of separation is high and the process was not operated on a commercial scale in this country. Graphite on the other hand was available in quantity, its use was familiar, and it was a reasonably efficient moderator. The principal drawback to graphite is that, because it is the least effective of the three materials in slowing neutrons, its use results in a large reactor. The size depends greatly upon the purity of the graphite. Impurities absorb neutrons and in fact a reactor will not work at all unless a certain minimum standard of purity is reached. As the purity is increased beyond this minimum, the size of the reactor decreases quite rapidly. Improvements in manufacturing methods were being studied which would, it was hoped, result in the production of considerably purer graphite. It was therefore decided to use graphite in the new reactor.

The choice of coolant was also determined largely by questions of neutron economy. Liquids generally are more efficient than gases at removing heat from a hot body, and several might be used as a reactor coolant, but they all have serious drawbacks. In the first place they all react with graphite, which would therefore have to be protected by lining the coolant channels with metal tubes instead of leaving them unlined as in Bepo. This additional metal would absorb more neutrons than could be tolerated. Then liquids themselves absorb neutrons. Apart from its effect on the neutron economy, this leads to a hazard when the neutron absorption of the coolant is greater than that of the moderator. Suppose a graphite-moderated reactor was cooled by ordinary water, which is a strong absorber of neutrons. If the flow of water through the reactor was interrupted, say by failure of the pumps, the water would boil and be blown out of the core; the loss of this neutron-absorbing material would cause a rapid increase in the neutron population and consequently a rapid rise in the power of the reactor, which might lead to overheating and damage.

Gases on the other hand tend to absorb neutrons far less than liquids because they contain many fewer atoms in each unit of volume. Therefore loss of a gaseous coolant from any cause would not result in a major increase in neutron density and there would be no risk of damage to the reactor. Moreover, several of the possible gases do not react appreciably with graphite and if one of these was used there would be no need to protect the moderator by means of metal tubes. The gas could be kept at the high pressure necessary for efficient heat transfer by enclosing the whole core in a big steel vessel and pumping the gas into one end and out of the other, a method which avoids introducing neutron absorbers into the core. In view of all these considerations, therefore, it was decided to use gas as coolant.

Thus early in the study three basic parameters of the reactor were fixed, viz. natural uranium fuel, graphite moderator, and compressed-gas cooling. It is interesting to see that a fresh examination *ab initio* of natural uranium power reactors led to the same conclusions as earlier studies, partly because economic factors, such as the availability of graphite compared with beryllium or heavy water, had not changed and partly because the use of enriched fuel was ruled out. Having made these decisions, the detailed work began. First came the question, what gas should be used as coolant.

THE CHOICE OF GAS

The principal requirements of the gas were that it should transfer heat efficiently, that it should capture neutrons to the least possible extent, that it should not break up chemically at the fairly high operating temperatures expected or as a result of bombardment by neutrons and other radiations, and (a vital point) that it should not react chemically with graphite or with metals in the core (including uranium, the alloy sheathing uranium, and the steel of the pressure vessel). Other considerations included cost and supply of the gas and pumping power required, although the latter depends principally on the pressure at which the gas is used.

Up to this time there was very little experimental information about the behaviour of possible gases at moderate temperatures, particularly in the presence of radiation. The few experiments before the feasibility study had been concerned mainly with the behaviour of air, as used in the Windscale piles, and had been aimed at measuring the rate at which oxygen in air reacted with graphite. These experiments had been done in the Chalk River reactor in conditions which simulated those within the Windscale pile. A few experiments had also been made on the reaction between graphite and carbon dioxide but most of these had been done without radiation.

The feasibility team therefore began thinking about different gases without much experimental evidence to help them. They cast their net wide. A dozen or more gases were considered ranging from hydrogen and helium, the lightest of all, through nitrogen to methane, ammonia, and sulphur dioxide. Many of these were rejected at once because it appeared from published information that radiation would break up their complex molecules. There remained a short list of some four gases. The best of these was helium, which is an efficient heat-transfer medium and is chemically inert and so would not react with graphite or metals. On the other hand, helium is expensive and is not available in quantity within the United Kingdom. A second possibility was hydrogen. This is readily available and is an excellent heat-transfer medium but has the disadvantage that it forms an explosive mixture with air; it also reacts with uranium. The next possibility was nitrogen, again a readily available gas with some good properties but having the drawbacks that it absorbs neutrons relatively strongly and probably reacts with graphite in the presence of radiation. Finally there was carbon dioxide. This gas is made in large quantities and is cheap, it is a better heat-transfer material than helium and, being denser, is easier to pump, and it does not absorb neutrons strongly. Its principal disadvantage, as far as was known at the beginning of the study, was that it reacts with graphite (i.e. carbon) to form carbon monoxide, and this reaction might lead to loss of graphite from the moderator.

On the face of it, carbon dioxide was the most hopeful gas but two questions remained to be answered by experiment. The first was, would the gas break up at elevated temperatures especially in the presence of radiation; the second was, how far would the reaction with carbon result in a loss of graphite from the moderator. These questions were put to the Chemistry Division at Harwell.

The first question was answered fairly quickly. Published data showed that carbon dioxide would be stable at much higher temperatures than expected in the reactor and earlier laboratory experiments had indicated that the effects of radiation would not be great. This was confirmed for high doses of radiation by exposing samples of very pure gas, sealed in silica vessels, in Bepo.

The reaction with graphite was a more complicated matter, however. This reaction consists in a combination between a molecule of carbon dioxide and an atom of carbon to form two molecules of carbon monoxide, another gas; the reverse reaction can also occur, the carbon monoxide breaking down into carbon and carbon dioxide. It was known from published data that, when there is no radiation, the reaction ultimately achieves an equilibrium, that is to say as much carbon and carbon dioxide combine to form carbon monoxide as carbon monoxide breaks down to form the other two products. At temperatures below 450°C this equilibrium occurs with a very small concentration of carbon monoxide and the rate of the reaction is negligibly small. As the temperature is increased the rate of the forward reaction increases, until around 600°C it is equivalent to a loss of about 1 per cent in a year of the total weight of graphite. In a reactor, loss of graphite from this cause would have two consequences. The first and obvious one is that, if it were excessive, it might endanger the graphite structure or at least limit its useful life. In addition there is the possibility that graphite would be eroded from one part of the core, where the temperature was high, and transferred either to cooler parts of the core or to cooler surfaces in the heat exchanger through which the gas would circulate.

The great unknown was the effect of radiation on this

reaction and this had to be determined experimentally by passing carbon dioxide over a sample of graphite in Bepo. The magnitude of the effect could then be determined from the loss in weight of the graphite, but it was calculated that for an experiment in Bepo this would involve measuring the weight change of about 14 millionths of a gramme of carbon a day. Now carbon is difficult to weigh accurately and experiments would have had to go on for months to give significant changes in weight. An alternative to weighing was to measure the rate at which carbon monoxide was produced. This could be done by a much more sensitive method called gas analysis. But this rate was still a very small quantity and the method would give erroneous answers if carbon monoxide crept in from any adventitious source. Consequently all impurities which might have led to the formation of carbon monoxide, directly or indirectly, had to be rigorously excluded from the apparatus. The equipment had therefore to be made entirely from glass and no grease could be allowed in any part of it.

To do the experiment a sample of graphite, surrounded by an electric furnace, was placed in a silica-glass vessel connected by silica tubes to an apparatus for circulating the carbon dioxide and from which samples of gas could be removed for analysis. The glass vessel was lowered through a hole into the centre of Bepo and the gas circulating and sampling equipment were left outside the pile, some 20 feet above. To avoid grease and oil the pump used to circulate the gas was made entirely of glass and none of the greased stopcocks customary in glass apparatus was allowed.

This experiment has been described in some detail because it illustrates the kind of research upon which major engineering decisions are based and the complications that may accompany an apparently straightforward measurement. The experiments showed that, although pile irradiation increased the rate of the reaction between carbon dioxide and graphite proportionally to the intensity of the radiation, the increased rate would not exceed the permissible limit. Accordingly, it was decided to go ahead with the design on the assumption that carbon dioxide would be used. At the same time it was felt that supplementary experiments ought to be made on an engineering scale; these will be described in Chapter 5.

THE FUEL ELEMENT

The next major advance was made in connexion with the uranium fuel. One cannot stoke a nuclear reactor with chunks of uranium in odd sizes and shapes, as one can shovel rough lumps of coal into an ordinary furnace. The uranium must be accurately machined to size, enclosed in a protective metal sheath or can, and disposed in a carefully calculated lattice in the graphite.

The uranium rod in its can, the fuel element as it is called, is the key component in a nuclear reactor and is one of the most difficult to design. Consider the requirements. In order to transmit the heat generated in the uranium through the metal can to the cooling gas, the can must make good thermal contact with the uranium on the inside and transfer heat efficiently to the gas on the outside. At the same time it must not be corroded either by the gas or by the uranium and, as with everything inside a reactor core, it must absorb neutrons to the least possible extent. Finally it must be mechanically strong at the high temperature of operation or the weight of the uranium inside would cause cracks and the can would cease to be effective in doing its job. An important requirement of the uranium rod inside the can is that it should retain its shape and size in spite of the changes in temperature, and the bombardment, by neutrons and other radiations, to which it is subjected during operation. This requirement is difficult to meet owing to the peculiar properties of the metal. As it is heated towards its melting point, its structure (i.e. the arrangement of atoms in the material) takes on no fewer than three forms and for each different structure the properties of the metal—its strength, expansion, heat conductivity, and so on— are different. Even more severe difficulties arise from the effects of neutron irradiation and of the stresses caused by intense local heating produced by fission. When a uranium atom splits in fission, the two new atoms formed charge through the metal with great energy, disturbing the orderly arrangement of atoms as they do so; even when they lose their energy and settle down in some vacant place in the atomic array they still affect the metal because two atoms different in nature from the original uranium have to be accommodated where only one atom existed before. Moreover, some of these fission product atoms are gases, e.g. xenon and krypton, and they may collect in pockets in the solid and distort it very greatly.

Thus two main problems face the fuel-element designer, viz. to find a canning metal capable of satisfying the criteria just outlined, and to devise treatments for uranium which will minimize the effects of radiation.

Aluminium had been used as the canning material in all British reactors existing in 1951. This metal meets the requirements well except that it is weak mechanically at high temperatures. For this reason other metals were considered for the power reactor. Of the half-dozen or so which have reasonably low neutron absorption, the best for high-temperature operation are the somewhat exotic beryllium and zirconium. But in 1951 neither was available except in small quantities and both were therefore rejected. However, at this time there was growing interest in the common metal magnesium. Recent measurements had shown that earlier information greatly exaggerated its neutron absorption, which was in fact only about a fifth that of aluminum. The metal was available in large quantities and with high purity. On the other hand, as far as was known, its mechanical properties were no better than those of aluminium and it was thought that there might be a risk of fire because magnesium burns readily in air, as anyone will know who has seen a flashlight photograph taken.

The metallurgists at Harwell felt, however, that the data

about magnesium were uncertain enough to justify fresh experimental investigation. Actually some preliminary experiments had been made in 1948 on the effects of temperature and radiation, with encouraging results, but the scale of the work had been too limited to enable it to be said with confidence that magnesium could be used in a reactor designed to work at a much higher temperature and neutron flux than Bepo. Work was now started to investigate the mechanical strength of magnesium at elevated temperatures and it was soon found that magnesium was superior, rather than inferior, to aluminium at proposed operating temperatures. At the same time some tentative experiments on the corrosion of magnesium by hot air and carbon dioxide were extended. Samples of metal were suspended from the arm of a chemical balance so that they hung inside a vessel through which the gas passed; the metal could be heated by a small electric furnace. Increases in weight indicated by the balance provided a measure of the corrosion. Experiments were made with very pure magnesium and with some standard alloys of the metal.

The results indicated that magnesium would resist corrosion well but it was felt that something better should be possible. When the measurements were related to a recently proposed theory of corrosion the conclusion was reached that magnesium alloys which included beryllium were likely to be more resistant than any of the materials tried so far. So, in collaboration with an industrial firm, a range of alloys containing beryllium and certain other elements was formulated and samples of each made by the firm. These alloys were tested at Harwell. Two of them turned out to be outstandingly good in resisting corrosion even by moist hot air, which is much more corrosive than carbon dioxide. Tests to find out whether the alloys would burn in air at high temperatures showed, as had earlier experiments with pure magnesium in carbon dioxide, that a protective film is formed round the molten metal and prevents burning. Other experiments confirmed that the alloys were as well behaved in carbon dioxide.

As will be shown in Chapter 5, the requirements of mass production necessitated further development and some changes in composition, but these important experiments established substantially the alloy used for the Calder Hall reactor. They enabled a major advance to be made in the reactor design because the low neutron absorption of the alloy permitted the use of a strong can, with good heat-transfer fins, without loss of reactivity.

HEAT TRANSFER OF THE CAN

The importance of this last point can be seen from the following considerations. The power developed by a reactor depends on the heat rating obtainable from the uranium, i.e. the amount of heat that can be extracted from each ton of metal. In a gas-cooled reactor this rating is rather low. It is determined by the efficiency with which heat is transferred from the surface of the fuel elements to the gas stream. Heat transfer can be increased by increasing the speed of the gas in the cooling channels, but then more power is needed to drive the gas blowers and this power has to be subtracted from the total generated in the plant; the net output may consequently be reduced. Heat transfer can also be increased by extending the surface of the cans, by fitting them with fins, but at the cost of neutron absorption in the fins; the low neutron absorption of magnesium enabled a greater fin area to be used than would have been possible with aluminium.

Not much was known about the effect of fin size and shape on heat transfer. The earliest experiments with finned cans had been made at Harwell in connexion with the Windscale piles. Originally the fins were longitudinal, i.e. they ran along the length of the can like a fish's dorsal fin, but these were found to be less efficient than expected. Then someone suggested putting the fins round the can, like the cooling fins on the cylinder of a motor-cycle engine. But in a motor cycle the

3. A completed heat exchanger.

4. The bottom dome of the pressure vessel at the beginning of its lift (left) and being lifted into the biological shield (right).

air blows transversely across the cylinder and therefore between the fins, whereas in a reactor the air is blown along the length of the can and therefore across the fins, an arrangement that on the face of it looked inefficient. Nevertheless it was tried, and it worked. More experiments were then made to determine variations in performance as changes were made in gas pressure and velocity, type of gas, temperature, size and spacing of fins, and so on. From the results curves were plotted from which designers could work out the optimum fins for a given set of conditions. Experiments along these lines are still going on, as will be seen in Chapter 5.

These three pieces of research—on the chemical compatibility of carbon dioxide, the corrosion-resistant magnesium alloys, and the properties of finned cans—were vital to the success of the project and are typical of the kind of work that is an essential part of a feasibility study. We must return now to the main line of development, the complete reactor and its associated power plant.

ENGINEERING DESIGN STUDIES

In designing a plant, two general, and broadly different, groups of engineering problems present themselves. The first group arises in establishing the optimum conditions in the plant; it is the essentially theoretical process that engineers call "optimizing the design" and it involves choosing, in the light of experience, a range of conditions over which operation might occur and then calculating the performance that would be achieved under these conditions. Since the light of experience in a new field like nuclear engineering is sometimes rather dim, there is often more guessing than exact estimating of conditions in these first stages of design; this is in fact the phase in which the intuitive approach is more important than the analytical, in which science plays second fiddle to art. The second and essentially practical group of problems is concerned with hardware, with for example finding ways of making a pressure vessel to the required size, of arranging a control system, of laying out heat exchangers to the best advantage. In this phase there is usually more experience to draw on but here, too, intuition is important.

In the optimizing calculations the nuclear power plant was considered in two sections, the reactor (the heat-producing section) and the boiler or heat exchanger (the heat-using section). In the reactor calculations, the overall size of the core and the quantity of fuel needed is worked out for different sizes of fuel element and different spacings between channels containing the elements. In doing this the neutron-absorbing properties of fuel, can, moderator, and coolant have to be assumed, and because these are not always known accurately there are often considerable uncertainties in the answers. Then the transfer of heat from fuel element to cooling gas in the central channel of the core (which is the hottest) is calculated for various pumping powers and other conditions. These results are used with the nuclear results to investigate the core as a whole and calculate the neutron density at different points throughout the core and hence find the weight of uranium needed. The flow of heat in the outer channels must also be worked out. On the heat-using side the best design of boiler involves choosing gas temperatures and flows, surface area in the boilers, gas pumping power, and steam pressure to give the best steam conditions consistent with long life for the plant and low capital costs. The results of all these calculations are then analysed to determine which set of conditions will give the greatest electrical power (and this is not the same as the greatest total heat) and the highest rate for converting uranium-238 to plutonium. For a reactor which is designed both to generate power and to produce plutonium, the optimum design is the one which gives the cheapest electricity for the greatest amount of plutonium.

From calculations of this sort sets of figures were derived which were in effect rough specifications for different reactors, and the most promising of these were studied in greater detail.

When these calculations revealed a lack of information about materials or components, experimental work, such as that already described on carbon-dioxide compatibility, had to be done.

While the optimizing calculations showed what to aim at, examination of the mechanical engineering problems showed how far these calculations could be translated into machinery. The conclusion from first calculations and thoughts about hardware resulted in an outline design which was described in a report of September 1951. In this it was proposed that the cylindrical graphite core should be mounted vertically in a steel pressure-resisting vessel, so that the fuel channels were vertical (see Figure 4). This proposal represented a major change, inasmuch as up to that time all British reactors had had horizontal channels, and it was not made without much heart-searching. The cooling gas was to be pumped into the bottom of the pressure vessel, pass upwards through the

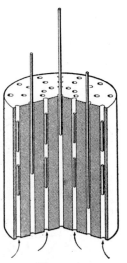

Figure 4.
Principle of vertical core arrangement.

channels, and emerge from the top through four large ducts which would lead it to four separate heat exchangers placed round the reactor. The hot gas was then to pass down these heat exchangers, boiling water on the way, and be pumped back to the pressure vessel by electrically driven blowers at the bottom. It is interesting to find that these are the essential features of the plant as it has been built at Calder Hall (see Figure 5).

At this time neither the coolant gas nor the canning material had been decided and the feasibility of many of the proposals had not been demonstrated. By the end of 1951, however,

most of the uncertainties about magnesium had been resolved
and it had been shown that a considerably improved grade of
graphite was likely to be available. For a time it was thought
that, as a consequence, a particularly compact reactor would

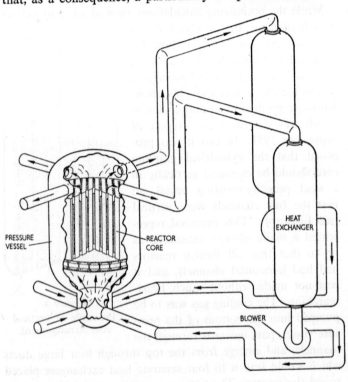

PRESSURE VESSEL

REACTOR CORE

HEAT EXCHANGER

BLOWER

REACTOR GAS FLOW

Figure 5.

be feasible and on this basis a suggestion was put forward for
a small nuclear plant to be built at Harwell to generate electricity and low-grade heat for the Establishment. This plant
was christened Pippa, a mnemonic based on the phrase
'pressurised pile for producing power and plutonium'. Later,

in June 1952, the small plant was found to be impracticable and attention was again turned to a large plant capable of generating about 150,000 kW of heat and suitable for a central generating station. Nevertheless the name Pippa stuck to the large plant.

During the first months of 1952 the study of the project was extended by bringing in engineers from industry. Over a year earlier the Central Electricity Authority (then the British Electricity Authority) had expressed interest in the development of nuclear power generation, but it was not until early 1952 that ideas on the subject were concrete enough to justify active participation by CEA engineers. Then in April the Authority seconded engineers to Harwell to work on the project, primarily on the heat-using side of the plant and particularly on the electrical equipment. At about the same time engineers from C. A. Parsons Ltd were seconded to the Establishment to work primarily on the gas circuits, especially on the gas blowers; later this firm studied the turbines. The Ministry of Works was brought in to give advice on architecture, the civil engineering, and the design of the pressure vessel. Finally, two more industrial firms joined the project; Babcock and Wilcox were invited to design the heat exchangers and Whessoe Ltd to design the pressure vessel.

This expanded team went to work on the large-reactor project. Experimental results became available that strengthened confidence in magnesium cans and carbon-dioxide coolant. Ways of overcoming engineering difficulties were discovered. Pressure vessel, heat exchanger, and blower problems were solved. One after another, at a rapidly increasing pace, uncertainties were resolved and design details established.

DESIGN OF VERTICAL CORE

It had been decided to build the core with the fuel channels vertical, principally because this made it easier to support such a great weight inside a pressure vessel. Vertical construction also simplified the problem of building a solid cylinder out of graphite bricks in such a way that the straightness of the clear channels would not be materially altered when the bricks became hot and expanded. Nevertheless, it was still necessary to consider many schemes in detail before an arrangement could be evolved that satisfied all requirements. Vertical arrangement also introduced complications. It was now necessary to find ways of supporting the uranium cartridges—or fuel elements—vertically, since they could no longer lie on their sides, and of putting the cartridges into (or taking them out of) the core through the pressure vessel. Other problems included operation of control rods through the pressure vessel and detection of faults in the fuel elements.

In the earlier horizontal reactors the core is charged and discharged by simply pushing the uranium cartridges through the channels from one end to the other, but this method is not so readily practicable with vertical channels. Moreover, to put cartridges into a pressure vessel they have to be passed through holes and it is clearly necessary to reduce the number of these holes or else the pressure vessel will not be strong enough to withstand the desired gas pressure. Accordingly it was decided to charge and discharge fuel elements from the same end of the vessel and to group the channels in the graphite so that a number could be served by a single hole through the pressure vessel. In this way the number of holes required to serve something like 1700 channels was reduced to a few more than a hundred. The machine designed to pass the cartridges through these holes into the required channel will be described in Chapter 3.

The operation of control rods presented a similar difficulty to the insertion of fuel elements. In reactors with horizontal channels, these rods move horizontally through holes in the shield and the machinery by which they were driven is in a cool place outside the shield. To avoid an excessive number of holes in the pressure vessel, it was decided to put the rods (which operate vertically) and their drive mechanisms inside the pressure vessel, the drive being placed in the coolest possible position, at the top of extension tubes from the main vessel. The functions of safety and control rods were combined by arranging that the rods are held to the control drive by means of a magnetic clutch; the reactor can then be shut down quickly by interrupting the current to the clutch and so releasing the rods and causing them to fall into the core. This arrangement ensures that any failure, including a failure in the electric supply, would result in immediate operation of the safety rods; it is an example of the 'fail to safety' principle of which nuclear engineers make frequent use.

THE PRESSURE VESSEL

The pressure vessel itself was a crucial component of the reactor; the feasibility of the project stood or fell by it. Indeed, even so fundamental a characteristic as the gas pressure was determined, not by pumping power or heat transfer, but by the maximum thickness thought to be practicable for the pressure vessel walls. An unusual problem like this called for specialist experience and Whessoe Ltd were therefore consulted.

A vessel of the size required was obviously too big to transport from the maker's factory to the site. It would therefore have to be fabricated from plates on site and the starting point in the design was the maximum thickness of steel plate which could be welded in such conditions. From their experience Whessoe Ltd decided that 2 inches was the thickest plate that could be tackled with certainty. On this basis they calculated that the vessel would safely withstand a gas pressure of 100 lb./sq. in., equivalent to seven times the pressure of the atmosphere, which was higher than the rather cautious estimate of possibilities made at Harwell.

The general arrangement proposed for the pressure vessel is shown in Figure. 6. It is a cylinder with a domed top and bottom. At the bottom of the lower dome is a cylindrical projection, the inlet manifold, into which four large ducts lead cool gas; corresponding outlet ducts for hot gas emerge

just below the upper dome. The upper dome itself is pierced
with the holes to which are attached stub tubes for charging
and discharging the reactor core. The number and size of

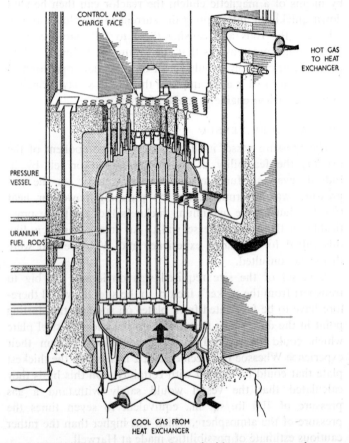

Figure 6.   Arrangement of core inside pressure vessel.

the openings that had to be left for the various ducts and
pipes greatly complicated the design because the stresses that
arise round an opening necessitate carefully calculated rein-
forcement of the edges. The hole for the inlet manifold,

5 (a). The inlet manifold of the pressure vessel on to which the bottom dome (Plate 4) is lowered. Sections of the gas ducts are lying ready to be welded on.

5 (b). The diagrid: after the centre sections have been added the diagrid is lowered into position. It is on this grid that the reactor core rests. The hot gas will leave through the holes at the top.

6 (*a*). Laying the graphite core: a completed layer showing the lattice of holes into which the fuel elements are lowered. On the wall, left, is one of the ports by which the hot gas will leave.

6 (*b*). Workman in clean clothing taps graphite block into place.

7. A bank of boiler tubes for the heat exchanger is thoroughly cleaned by shot-blasting.
(Note the heat-transfer fins formed by thousands of projecting studs welded to the tube's surface. See also Figure 8.)

8. Looking down into the heat-exchanger shell: banks of boiler tubes being placed in position.

probably the largest ever proposed in a pressure vessel, was particularly awkward.

The reactor core rests inside the cylinder on a grid of steel girders welded to a circular ring girder; this structure, the diagrid, is supported by brackets welded to the inside of the lower dome. The diagrid had to take the weight of the core— over 1000 tons—without bending more than ¼ inch at the centre; the thirty-five simultaneous equations involved in the design were solved with the aid of an electronic computer. The weight on the diagrid had to be transmitted through the walls of the vessel to supports outside and these supports had to be so arranged that they would not stress the vessel when it expanded and contracted with changes in temperature. The designers drew upon their experience of building gas-holders and pressure vessels for oil refineries to work out a system of struts with curved ends, which met the requirements. A speci-fication for the steel for the vessel was drawn up in con-sultation with the steel manufacturers. This steel had to be capable of being welded to the highest standards and to be exceedingly ductile, because no one knew quite how much it would become hardened by the action of radiation. Ways had to be found to minimize corrosion by carbon dioxide and the content of cobalt had to be kept to a minimum because this element becomes radioactive under irradiation.

HEAT EXCHANGERS AND PLANT CONTROL

The next major components were the heat exchangers or boilers, in which water is turned into steam by heat trans-ferred from the hot carbon dioxide. To most people steam is a white cloud coming from a boiling kettle; this is simply water vapour at the pressure of the atmosphere and the tem-perature of boiling water. To an engineer this is wet and low-grade steam, of little use for driving machinery. He needs what he calls high-grade steam, that is steam at high tempera-ture and therefore high pressure, produced by boiling water in closed vessels. The higher the temperature the more efficiently the engine will work. The designer therefore aims at a boiler which produces the greatest quantity of steam at the highest possible temperature. In a reactor like Pippa the maximum boiler temperature is fixed by the temperature of the gas as it comes from the core. When steam is raised at high pressure not very much heat is removed from the gas and it would leave the boiler still pretty hot. This would not matter if all one was interested in was the quality of the steam, but the gas leaving the boiler has to be pumped back into the reactor and the power required to drive the blowers that do this is determined by the temperature of the cooled gas; the hotter the gas the greater the power required. This blower power must be debited against the power generated in considering the net output of the plant and must therefore be kept small. Hence the cooled gas temperature must be a minimum. There is thus a conflict between requirements for best steam conditions and requirements for economic operation. The problem is to determine the optimum compromise.

The Harwell team put a tentative proposal for steam generation to Babcock and Wilcox Ltd. This firm had ready a solution in principle based on the work they did in 1947. The many hundreds of calculations which they had then made had shown that it was desirable to raise steam at two different pressures, in a so-called dual-pressure cycle. The method was as follows. The hot gas from the reactor was first to go through a heat exchanger in which good-quality steam would be generated at the highest possible pressure. The gas leaving this section of the heat exchanger would still be comparatively hot. It would then be passed through a second section of the heat exchanger in which rather low-grade steam would be generated, the steam conditions being determined by the temperature of the emergent gas, which in its turn would be determined by the desired circulator power. The steam of these two grades was then to be fed to a turbine having high-pressure and low-pressure cylinders. The high-pressure steam would produce about 65 per cent of the power generated, but the low-pressure steam would provide a useful contribution and would raise the overall efficiency of the plant considerably.

The dual-pressure steam cycle has an important advantage in connexion with controlling the plant as a whole, especially if it is necessary suddenly to shut down either the reactor, perhaps from a fault in a fuel element, or the turbine, if for example, the grid transmission line failed. Whatever the cause, it is highly undesirable that the temperature of the reactor should be allowed to change suddenly because this would cause thermal stresses that might damage the structure. The plant control is therefore arranged so that the temperature of the core can be kept nearly constant whatever the load, except of course when the reactor is shut down slowly to allow fuel elements to be replaced. Constant temperature is achieved by doing two things; the rise in temperature of the gas as it goes through the core is kept constant, regardless of the rate at which heat is being generated, by varying the speed of the gas circulators and hence the rate at which the gas flows through the core; and the temperature of the gas entering the core is kept constant, regardless of the heat supplied to the boilers, by varying the steam pressure in the low-pressure section of the boiler (the higher the pressure, the less the heat removed from the gas and therefore the higher the emergent gas temperature). This double control results in a closer control of temperature, and is considerably more efficient, than would be possible in a system which depended only on varying the gas flow.

Associated with the control system is the so-called dump condenser. This is a drum filled with tubes through which cold water flows; steam passed into the drum is condensed by the cold tubes. A valve enables all, or part, of the steam from the boiler to be diverted to the dump condenser instead of going to the turbine. In this way the steam load of the boiler can be kept constant regardless of the electrical load of the turbo-alternator; the reactor can in fact continue to operate at full power even when the turbo-alternator is idle. The dump condenser also enables the turbines to be started and run up with the reactor at power.

The steam turbines and the gas circulators were designed by C. A. Parsons Ltd, who were the other main contractors in the feasibility study. These units will be described at greater length in Chapter 3.

THE OUTCOME OF THE FEASIBILITY STUDY

Such were the main components of the nuclear power plant described in the final report of the feasibility study. Together they comprised a system capable of generating over 50,000 kW of electric power, at a cost not greater than a penny a unit, and of producing at the same time substantial quantities of plutonium. As far as the design team could see, construction of the plant was feasible and reasonable; although not complete, the experiments and engineering design work on fuel elements, chemical compatibility of structural materials, reactor heat transfer, and major components had been taken far enough to show that important snags were unlikely to reveal themselves. In short, feasibility had been established.

The feasibility, or design, study is an important concept in a new field of engineering. It will be seen that a feasibility study begins with a general review of possible plants, from which the most promising one is picked out. Then comes a down-to-earth assessment of all the problems that would be encountered if the chosen type of plant were built. The study is complete only when reasonably detailed solutions to the problems, supported as necessary by experiment, have been reached. There is hard thinking in these studies about all aspects of the design; they are not based on unproven assumptions or on 'solutions in principle' but on exact measurement and detailed engineering experience. The outcome, though not a complete engineering design, is much more than a general proposal; it shows how the parts of the plant can be made, what the economics of operation should be, and where further development is needed.

DECISION TO BUILD

The Pippa plant had been envisaged as a station for the Central Electricity Authority and at the time the report was written the possibility of building one on a CEA site was being considered in detail. In the meantime the Chiefs of Staff had asked for an increase in production of military plutonium, and to meet this requirement the Department of Atomic Energy Production in the Ministry of Supply (now the Industrial Group of the Atomic Energy Authority) had to consider building an additional plutonium-producing reactor. The Department did not want to build another Windscale pile because that design was obsolete. It was obviously better to take a step forward and build a reactor of the Pippa type even although power generation had to be made secondary to plutonium production; operation of the reactor would still give a net gain in power which could be fed to the grid and would also yield a handsome dividend in experience of power-producing gas-cooled reactors. Accordingly in February 1953 the Government accepted a recommendation that a single Pippa-type reactor should be built to produce military plutonium and electric power. The Industrial Group at Risley were to take over engineering design and construction of the plant from the stage at which the Harwell design team had left it. How they did so and what the construction involved will be described in the next chapter.

CHAPTER THREE

The Building of "Pippa"

The construction of the new reactor was transferred to the Industrial Group because building factories is their business. Harwell is a research establishment; its job is to establish fundamental principles and extend the boundaries of knowledge and it had done this by supplying the scientific data and general engineering design of the proposed nuclear power plant. It was now for the Industrial Group to turn these ideas into steel and concrete. In order to use the detailed knowledge acquired during the feasibility study, some of the engineers engaged on it were transferred from Harwell to Risley and the principal contractors agreed to continue their work on the individual parts of the plant.

THE DESIGN ORGANIZATION

Following its usual practice, the Industrial Group set up a team under a design engineer who was responsible for the design and construction of the whole plant. This engineer had behind him all the resources of the Industrial Group, the special skills of its other designers, its contracting and supply organization, its research and development branch, its operating department with their wide experience of atomic energy factories, and its administrative machinery. He was also backed by the research knowledge and experience of Harwell and of the engineering firms engaged on the project. His job was to direct and control every aspect of the work and his responsibility to produce an efficient factory at the appointed time and at a cost within the approved estimate.

The design team had a total strength of about seventy and these were supported by several times that number from the specialist service groups; an integral part of the team was a group from Parolle Ltd, working on the steam side of the plant. The team was responsible for the design of every part of the plant, from the smallest component to the largest installation. Some parts were contracted out and then the design office closely controlled the contractor's work. Engineering design, supply, construction, erection, cost, time schedule—for each the design engineer had ultimate responsibility. There was an enormous amount to do and the pace was hot —the design team began work on 7 April 1953 and less than $3\frac{1}{2}$ years later their £16,500,000 plant will go into full operation.

The first thing to be done was to work out a programme for the construction. The designer had been given the date at which the plant must begin operation. This was the one immutable figure in all his planning; nothing might be allowed to alter it. From his experience he could estimate the time required for each major stage in building the plant—design, construction, operating trials. By relating these periods of time to the target date, he could draw up a programme showing the dates on which each phase must begin for each section of the plant. This analysis is presented in the form of a diagram in which the time span for each phase is shown as a thick horizontal line; each line ends at a vertical line corresponding to the target date. The broad programme is further broken down into the constituent parts of each section of the plant, and dates are determined for every phase of the work on each part. All these separate programmes are fitted into the overall programme in a way that ensures that no item is held up because another on which it depends has not been completed. This overall planning is an essential feature of the Risley method of working.

Detailed planning does not mean that all the information needed for design or construction is necessarily available when the plan is drawn up. On the contrary, when the object is to build a plant in the shortest possible time, and when the plant is of a kind new to engineering, it is unavoidable that many details shall be vague at the beginning. It is true that because the feasibility study had been so thorough, there were fewer uncertainties in building Calder Hall than in building the Windscale factory. Nevertheless there were still many unknowns and research continued both at Harwell and at the Research and Development Branch of the Industrial Group, to extend and consolidate the work done during the feasibility study. At the site, foundations were laid and buildings erected without knowing exactly what was to go into them. The one certainty in the mind of all concerned was that the finished plant would work.

THE SITE

It was decided to build the new plant alongside the Windscale plutonium factory. The possibility of extending this factory had been anticipated some time earlier by the purchase of land on the east of the River Calder. This land had formed part of a farm belonging to Calder Hall, a manor house built in the seventeenth century, and the factory takes its name from river and farm. The country is open and close to the sea, with gentle slopes inland which lead the eye towards the background of the Lake District hills. Access to the site is by road over a specially-built bridge across the Calder. There is no railway and none is needed. A year's fuel for a nuclear power station can be brought in a dozen or so lorries, compared with the thousands of railway wagons that are needed to supply a coal-fired station. Nor are there any ashtips. The discharged fuel elements, with their contained nuclear ash, are taken in lorries to the chemical plant at Windscale where they are treated to remove fission products and plutonium.

When design began only one reactor was authorized but it was decided to plan for two, and a second was in fact authorized a few months later. The Harwell layout was therefore opened out a little. The reactors were housed in two buildings separated from each other by a third building containing the turbines and electric alternators. The general

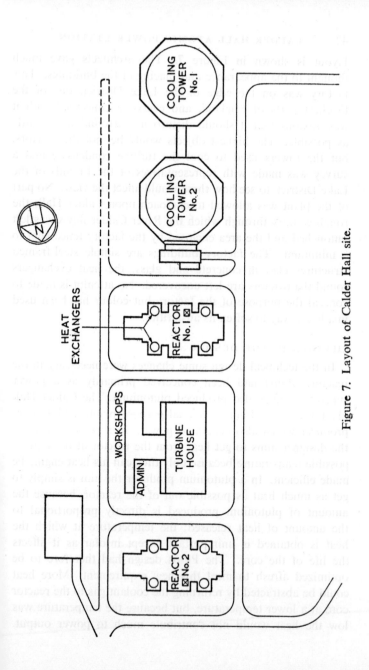

Figure 7. Layout of Calder Hall site.

layout is shown in Figure 7. The architects gave much thought to the appearance and placing of the buildings. This factory was on the edge of the Lake District, one of the loveliest parts of England, and everyone concerned with it was anxious that it should disturb its surroundings as little as possible. The highest objects would be, not the reactors, but the towers used to cool the turbine condensate and a survey was made with representatives of the Friends of the Lake District, to see how these would affect the view. No part of the plant was allowed to encroach upon Calder Hall; the rough country through which the River Calder flows was left untouched and the area enclosed by the factory fence kept to a minimum. The factory buildings are simple steel-framed structures clad in concrete and glass; the heat exchangers round the reactors are left uncovered. No attempt is made to conceal the purpose of the factory but colour has been used in a lively way to soften its austerities.

CHANGES IN THE DESIGN

In the technical design some changes were necessary in the reactor. Pippa had been conceived primarily as a power generator which also produced plutonium. The Calder Hall plant was to be built as a dual-purpose plant, a plutonium producer which also generated power. In a power generator the designer aims to get heat from the reactor at the highest possible temperature because only thus can his heat engine be made efficient. In a plutonium producer the aim is simply to get as much heat as possible out of the reactor, because the amount of plutonium produced is directly proportional to the amount of heat released; the temperature at which the heat is obtained is unimportant except insofar as it affects the life of the core. The Pippa design had therefore to be optimized afresh to meet this new requirement. More heat could be abstracted by returning the coolant gas to the reactor core at a lower temperature, but because the temperature was low the heat would not contribute much to power output.

However, when the engineers considered the optimization of the heat exchangers at the new conditions, they showed that the dual-pressure cycle could be adapted so that the extra plutonium would be forthcoming without losing electrical power. The new steam conditions were not as good as the original ones because they led to a much larger flow of low-pressure steam; this meant that physically larger, and therefore more expensive, boilers and turbines were necessary. In fact the price paid for the greater plutonium production was an increase in the capital cost of the steam plant and turbines for a given electrical output.

Having established the new conditions, the design could go ahead. The reactor itself was little changed but the steam side was considerably affected and with it much of the ancillary plant. Some idea of the technical effort involved in this work may be gained from a remark by one of Babcock and Wilcox's engineers, in presenting new proposals for the optimum steam cycle, to the effect that earlier calculations had given them the feel of the plant so they had now to make only forty sets of fresh calculations.

The heart of the plant is of course the reactor. From the outside this looks like a great boiler drum, the size of two houses stacked one above the other, domed top and bottom, with a forest of pipes sticking out, like pins in a pin-cushion, from the upper dome; stuck to the bottom dome is another drum, small by the standards of the main one (not much bigger than a railway locomotive), into which run four large gas pipes, whilst just below the pin-cushion four more gas pipes emerge to carry off the hot gas to the heat exchangers. Inside this assembly is the reactor core with over a thousand tons of graphite, just over ten thousand uranium rods, and all the paraphernalia of control and operation. The core becomes intensely radioactive in operation and even the thick steel of the pressure vessel is not able to stop flying neutrons or gamma-rays. The reactor is therefore surrounded by a concrete shield seven feet thick, which reduces the intensity of all radiations to a harmless level. The shield is not circular in section, like the reactor, but is octagonal because this shape is easier to construct in concrete. Between the concrete octagon and the pressure vessel is placed a shield of steel plates, six inches thick, to protect the concrete from heat generated from the attenuation of the radiation from the reactor; this thermal shield is separated from the concrete by a gap a few inches wide, up which air is blown to cool the shield. This air is discharged through two steel stacks on the roof of the pile building. At the four corners of the foundation supporting the octagon are four concrete plinths upon which four heat exchangers are placed. The octagon and its reactor are covered by a steel-framed building and similar buildings connected to it contain the control room, fuel store, discharge machinery, and various ancillary plant.

The general scheme of construction was to build a foundation raft and upon it the octagonal shield. Simultaneously the pressure vessel would be fabricated in sections and the sections lifted by crane into the completed shield, where they would be welded together. When the pressure vessel was completed, the roof of the shield would be put on. This course was adopted to save time; the shield and pressure vessel are both major constructional jobs and had the work not been overlapped, a great deal of time, a year at least, would have been lost. In the meantime the four heat exchangers were to be assembled and erected on their four plinths around the reactor. The plan was simple. We shall see what it cost in engineering effort in the following paragraphs.

CIVIL ENGINEERING

The first people to start work on a new factory are the civil contractors, who open the site, make roads, lay foundations, and provide services. After this come reinforced concrete construction, erection of steelwork, cladding of buildings,

and finally installation of machinery. The main civil contractors at Calder Hall were Taylor Woodrow Construction
Ltd; steelwork was erected by Alexander Findlay & Co, and
machinery installed by Mathew Hall Ltd.

Major construction began with excavation for the reactor
foundations. The reactor with its shield and associated buildings weighs 22,000 tons; it rests on a reinforced concrete
raft 11 feet thick by 130 feet long by 104 feet wide which adds
nearly another 10,000 tons to the total weight on the subsoil.
It was essential that this raft should not move or settle when
completed or the biological shield on it might crack. The
concrete had therefore to be of high and uniform quality
throughout, and had to be placed in such a way as to minimize
movement and shrinking. Similar demands for very large
quantities of concrete mixed and poured to unusually high
standards recurred throughout the construction, especially in
the biological shield. A large plant was therefore erected for
handling materials and mixing the concrete, and special
arrangements made for transporting and pouring the mixed
concrete. Quality was assured by taking frequent samples
and checking their composition, density, and mechanical
properties in a specially-built laboratory.

The octagonal shield is made of reinforced concrete and is
some 88 feet high and 46 feet across inside. The specification
required that the inside walls should not depart from the
vertical throughout their height by more than a quarter of an
inch. This degree of accuracy is much beyond the ordinary
standards of civil engineering. In order to attain it a "spider",
or octagonal tower of steel girders, was erected the full height
of the shield; this was made adjustable to the required
accuracy and used to support accurately-made wooden shut-
tering against which concrete was poured. In order to avoid
gaps and variations in density, great care was taken in making
joints between lifts and in pouring and vibrating the concrete,
especially round the many holes for ducts and pipes that pass
through the shield.

PRESSURE VESSEL

The decision to build the pressure vessel in sections and lift the completed sections into the octagon meant that very heavy lifting tackle was needed. A 100-ton derrick was used, built on a steel tower 90 feet high and known on the site as the 'big stick'. The derrick was steadied by eight guy wires 800 feet long, anchored to 30-ton concrete blocks. In order to make sure that none of these guy wires would get in the way of construction at any stage, a scale model of the complete factory was made and strings put on it to simulate the guys and so enable their positions to be settled.

The provision of sufficient and adequate lifting tackle is of major importance to quick construction and the big stick was only the largest of many cranes, of all sizes, on the Calder Hall site. One observer remarked that wherever you were on the site, it never seemed necessary for a man to lift anything heavier than a hammer; there was always a crane handy. Lifting arrangements, especially for the heavy reactor items, dominated construction and had therefore to be considered at the outset of design.

The pressure vessel was assembled from steel plates fabricated and shaped at the manufacturers' works; each plate was checked for flaws by ultrasonic methods. The edges of the plates were prepared for welding by bevelling them. This operation was performed by a planing machine on the flat plates, which were then rolled to the curvature required for the central cylindrical sections. For the domed ends, however, the plates were curved in two directions and it was necessary to design a special machine for preparing the edges of these.

The finished plates were transported to the site and there welded together to form five sections already mentioned, the upper and lower domes, two intermediate cylindrical sections, and the diagrid. These sections were built up on wheels, running on railway lines; completed units were then wheeled to the reactor building ready to be lifted. Stiffening tubes

were welded across the inside of each section to prevent distortion during the lift. The lower dome was assembled
upside-down for ease in welding. It had therefore to be
turned over and then raised 125 feet in the air, swung over
the octagon, and lowered gently and accurately into its
appointed place. It was fascinating to watch the apparent
ease with which these 80- or 90-ton units, each the size of a
large bungalow, were moved by the great crane; it is not
difficult to imagine how high a degree of skill was required of
the crane driver. After the lower dome the first cylindrical
section was put in, to rest exactly on the edge of the inverted
dome. The two units were then welded together. The second
cylindrical section followed and after it had been welded in
place the diagrid was lowered into the cylinder and placed on
its brackets on the inside of the lower dome.

Finally came the upper dome, the pin-cushion. This was
the most complicated part of the structure because of the
stub tubes. These tubes had to register with the channels in
the graphite core inside the pressure vessel and with holes
through the concrete roof (yet to be built) that would cover
the octagonal shields. They had therefore to be placed very
accurately on the dome, a requirement that demanded highly
developed techniques in assembly and welding.

It will be seen that the construction of the pressure
vessel involved a great deal of welding of the highest
grade. The contractor employed only his most experienced
welders and every inch of weld was examined by X-rays
to the exacting requirements of Lloyds class 1 standards.
Some of the welds took many hours of continuous work to
complete.

Welding always sets up stresses in metal and these, if not
removed, might cause failure, especially in a structure subjected to high pressure. These stresses can be relieved by
heating the steel to a high temperature. So after the pressure
vessel had been completed it was covered with a sort of tea
cosy of thermal insulation and inside was built the largest

electric fire ever made—a network of 2-inch steel tubes forming a giant parrot's cage—into which some 1500 kW of electric power were fed. Slowly the vessel was heated until after nearly three days it reached a temperature of 600°C— red heat. It was kept at this temperature for a day and then the current was switched off and the structure allowed to cool slowly. Up to the present this is the largest vessel that has been stress relieved by this method.

After stress relief came a pressure test. Usually pressure vessels are tested by filling them with water at the desired pressure but the weight of water in a vessel of this size would have imposed excessive stresses on the supports. It was therefore decided to make the test with air instead. To strategic points of the vessel were attached strain gauges and joints were painted with a brittle lacquer that would crack along the line of any strain that developed. All holes were closed by welding steel sheets over them and air was pumped in to raise the pressure in small steps. All gauges were read and lacquered joints inspected before each step increase in pressure. As a final check the vessel was evacuated to a pressure equivalent to a tenth of that of the atmosphere. The satisfactory completion of these tests was a landmark in the construction, for they showed the designers that their vessel would cope safely with the design pressure.

With the pressure vessel completed, the next task was to put the roof on the biological shield. This was made of reinforced concrete 8 feet thick and weighed many hundreds of tons. It had to be truly flat on the underside; not more than $\frac{1}{4}$-inch departure from level was permissible. To achieve this a method developed for Windscale piles was used. The walls of the shield were spanned by a number of Bailey bridge girders from which were suspended steel plates welded together to form permanent shutterings. The plates were given an upward curvature so calculated that when the concrete was poured above them its weight caused a deflection that exactly cancelled the curvature and resulted in

9. The pins in the pincushion—header tubes, on the top dome of the pressure vessel, through which fuel elements are loaded into the core. Each of these tubes serves a number of channels in the graphite core.

10. The tubes in Plate 8 in their completed state: they are now embedded in 8 foot of concrete which forms the shield roof. Parts of two charge machines can be seen at the sides of the picture.

11. The top of the reactor showing the charge/discharge machines. The charge machine (rear left) is less heavily shielded than the discharge machine (rear centre) which has to handle highly active spent fuel cartridges.

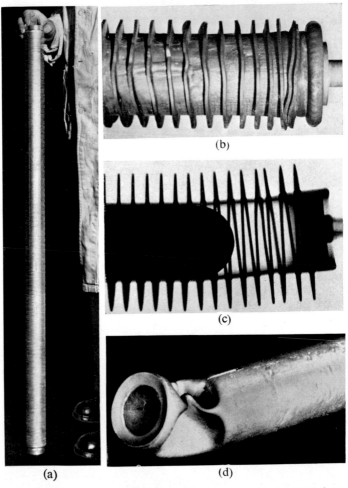

12 (*a*). The fuel element is a rod of unanium inside a magnesium-alloy can. It has cooling fins like those of a motor-cycle engine; (*b*). Distortion of the can caused by ratchetting; (*c*). X-rays show how the can has expanded more than the uranium, (*d*). Severe distortion in an experimental (finless) can caused by ratchetting. Repeated heating and cooling may damage a fuel element by 'ratchetting'. Means for preventing this have been embodied in the Calder Hall fuel elements.

a flat under-surface. Over a hundred holes pass through this roof to register with the tubes in the pressure vessel below.

STACKING THE GRAPHITE CORE

Now came one of the most involved operations, the construction of the active heart of the station, the reactor core, inside the pressure vessels. This core is 27 feet high and 35 feet in diameter and is pierced by nearly 1700 channels. It is made up of 58,000 machined graphite blocks and tiles interlocked in such a way as to ensure that, whatever dimensional changes the structure may undergo during the life of the reactor, the spacing and size of the fuel and control-rod channels will not be disturbed. The structure is worked out layer by layer and the position, shape, and size of every block and tile shown on a series of layer drawings, each block being identified in its position by a number. The blocks are machined to a tolerance of 0·002 inch.

It was essential that no impurities which might absorb neutrons should be allowed in the completed core. The graphite blocks were therefore machined under conditions comparable in cleanliness with the aseptic conditions of an operating theatre. Each completed block was marked with its identifying number, vacuum cleaned, and packed in a cardboard box for transport to the reactor. The reactor pressure vessel was cleaned inside and protected from corrosion by air conditioning. After this had been done, stringently clean conditions were maintained inside throughout the stacking and other work. All the workmen had to change their clothes completely before entering the sealed vessel and spectacles, wrist-watches, and similar personal property were checked to ensure that they were not inadvertently left inside the reactor. Certain metals such as brass were prohibited. Inside the electrically lit, air-conditioned vessel a man worked in isolation from the outside world, unaware of day or night, surgically clean on a pile of coal-black graphite.

When 60,000 bricks have to be built into a structure the size of a house, no part of which may depart from designed size by more than a hundredth of an inch, unusual precautions are necessary to control accuracy. Inspection of work was unusually thorough. In fact, of the three shifts working through a twenty-four-hour day on stacking, one was given over wholly to inspection. Supervision and inspection were similarly important in other parts of the construction where high accuracy or close control were necessary; examples are laying the concrete for the octagon and the erection of the heat exchangers.

CHARGE-DISCHARGE MACHINERY

To complete the picture of the reactor three major ancillaries will be described here, though they were in fact installed rather later in the construction. The first is the charge-discharge machinery. Fuel elements (the uranium rods in their cans) are put into or removed from the core through a movable chute or snout that enters the pressure vessel through one of the tubes at the top and is placed so that it pokes into a channel; an electrically-operated grab at the end of a steel cable is lowered through the chute and automatically seizes the first cartridge. The cable is then wound in and the cartridge deposited in a shielded steel basket, the operation being repeated until the channel is empty. The chute is then moved to the next channel and so on until all the channels in the group have been cleared.

The operating equipment for this purpose is mounted in a discharge machine which runs on rails on the shield roof. When a basket is filled with cartridges the machine is moved until it is over a well at the side of the building; the full basket is then lowered down the well into a tank filled with water. Fresh cartridges are loaded into the empty channels by a second, charge, machine operating in the same manner as the discharge machine. Two machines of each type are provided for each reactor.

DETECTION OF FAULTY FUEL ELEMENTS

The second important ancillary is the equipment for detecting and locating faulty fuel elements. A puncture in the can of a fuel element must be detected immediately otherwise fission products escaping from the uranium into the gas stream would contaminate the heat exchangers and other parts of the gas circuit. If such contamination were possible it would be necessary to build concrete shields around the gas circuit and heat exchangers; by preventing contamination this necessity is avoided and construction greatly simplified. The detection method is simple in principle and is so sensitive that a puncture no bigger than a pin-hole can be readily detected. Small-bore stainless-steel tubes, one to each channel, carry a trickle of gas from the channel to a radio-activity detector in the adjacent control building. The detector sniffs at each pipe in turn, covering all channels in half an hour; if the level of radioactivity in the gas rises above the average background then fission products must be escaping from a faulty can. Activity is recorded continuously and an exceptionally high level is made to ring a warning bell. The complication and practical difficulty of the system will be realized when it is recalled that there are 1700 channels for each of which a separate sniffing pipe is needed. There are 45 miles of steel tubing in this equipment, every inch of which had to be fabricated and installed under clean conditions.

CONTROL ARRANGEMENTS

Thirdly, we must consider the control arrangements. There are two main control points in the plant, one for the reactor and one for the generating equipment. From the point of view of the reactor, the steam and electrical plant are regarded simply as a cooling system. From the point of view of the electrical control (which is situated in the turbine building), the reactor plant is regarded simply as a source of steam which can be used for generating electricity or rejected to dump, according to the demands of the electricity grid.

The general method of reactor control has already been described in connexion with the steam cycle. Nuclear power level is controlled by moving neutron-absorbing boron steel rods in and out of the core; temperature rise through the core is kept constant by varying the rate at which the gas flows, whilst temperature of the gas entering the core is kept constant by varying the pressure of steam in the low-pressure boiler. There are thus three main controls, one for the neutron-absorbing rods, one for the speed of the gas circulators, and one for the low-pressure boiler. These controls, together with power level indicators and an over-riding control for the safety function of the rods, are placed on a desk at which the controlling operator sits. Beyond the desk is a horse-shoe of wall panels. The centre panel carries an outline of the plant showing the reactor and its four heat exchangers; within each outline are instruments indicating, for the reactor, the positions of control rods and the pressure of gas in the pressure vessel, and for each heat exchanger, the flow and pressure of gas and of steam. Other panels display temperatures of various points of the plant, state of the different auxiliary circuits, and indications of faults. The system is such as one would find in any well-engineered plant and is unusual only in so far as the properties of the plant itself are unusual.

The control system is designed to ensure safety in normal operations and also to provide safeguards in an emergency. It must be emphasized, however, that this is an exceptionally safe plant by any standards because the natural-uranium gas-cooled reactor has inherent safety characteristics which have been exploited to the full in Calder Hall designs. Because the coolant gas does not absorb neutrons, an accident resulting in a rapid loss of coolant would not cause power to rise and the reactor to overheat before the control rods could be operated. Moreover, it is a property of the reactor that the reactivity decreases as the temperature rises; this again is an inherent safety-valve, since any circumstances that caused a rise in temperature would also cause a decrease in power tending to offset the rise. In any event, with such a large core, temperature changes are slow. Finally, carbon dioxide is neither poisonous nor inflammable—on the contrary it blankets a fire. All these factors assure a natural safety, in addition to the safety built in by design of the control system and by providing radioactivity indicators.

INSTRUMENTS

Many special instruments were necessary to provide the information on which the control system operates. These included gas-flow meters and pressure indicators, humidity indicators, and temperature-measuring equipment for all parts of the plant including selected fuel elements in the core. For some purposes standard equipment could be used but frequently special instruments had to be developed by Risley in collaboration with industry. One important group of instruments is concerned with measuring the operating power of the reactor in terms of the neutron population (or neutron flux) in the core. These instruments were designed at Harwell and developed and manufactured by industry. The Calder Hall reactor presented several new problems to the designers of nuclear instruments. One of the most formidable of these arose from the fact that the core was inside a pressure vessel where everything would be very hot. In other reactors it had been possible to find cool, or fairly cool, places for the measuring equipment, and no one liked the idea of trying to make reliable electrical measurements in hot high-pressure gas. The difficulty was overcome in the following way. The quantity to be measured, and upon which the power of the reactor depends, is the flux of thermal neutrons in the core. This flux is normally measured by an instrument called an ionization chamber, placed in the graphite near the edge of the core. As has been said this position was unsuitable in the Calder Hall reactor and the thick steel walls of the pressure vessel tend to absorb the thermal neutrons, so the chamber could not be used outside the vessel. However, the steel does not stop the fast neutrons. It was therefore proposed to put a large block of graphite just outside the pressure vessel; fast neutrons entering this block would be slowed to thermal energies and could then be detected by an ionization chamber in the block. This arrangement would be about a thousand times as sensitive as a scheme that depended on measuring fast neutrons.

Another innovation is a method of measuring the nuclear power even when the reactor is shut down. In this condition no chain reaction takes place but because a certain proportion of the uranium atoms undergo spontaneous fission, there is still a small neutron flux corresponding to a power of about a thousandth of a watt. As the reactor is started the neutron flux increases until the chain reaction is established, which happens at a flux corresponding to perhaps 10 watts. During the start-up operation, therefore, measurements of flux are needed at an extremely low level, lower than can be measured with instruments suitable for use in a factory. It was therefore decided to boost the neutron flux at shut-down by putting a strong source of neutrons in the reactor core; this would raise the average flux to a level corresponding to about 1 watt and variations about this average could be readily measured by industrial instruments. The sources used are made of antimony and beryllium. Neither of these is normally radioactive, but after it has been exposed to neutrons in a reactor some of the antimony is transmuted into the isotope antimony-124; this isotope is radioactive and gives off gamma-rays which knock neutrons out of beryllium nuclei. Thus the sources are, in effect, made by the reactor in which they are used, a device which greatly simplifies and cheapens their manufacture.

After the chain reaction has started the neutron flux increases as the reactor power is run up until, at full power, it corresponds to about 200,000,000 watts. Thus from shut-down to full power the flux to be measured varies over a range from 1 to 200,000,000, which is much more than can be covered by a single instrument, even with the neutron-boosting sources at low level. Actually six sets of instruments of different types are used, arranged so that at any power level at least two types are indicating power. At the very lowest levels two detectors are used, ionization chambers and boron-trifluoride pulse counters; the latter are intended principally to give indications immediately after shut-down, when the intense gamma radiation from the pressure vessel tends to mask neutrons in an ionization chamber.

Associated with power measurement is a meter that indicates the rate at which the power level is changing, the reactor period as it is called. This is particularly valuable during start-up, when it is important that the reactor shall not be run up too quickly. The period meter is arranged so that a warning is given to the operator if the rate exceeds a preset value. Other electronic instruments include shut-down amplifiers, which cause the shut-off rods to operate if power exceeds a given level, and the monitoring part of the gear for detecting faulty fuel elements. Standard monitors are available to check radiation levels wherever men may be working.

GAS CIRCUIT AND BLOWERS

The hot gas is led from the pressure vessel to the heat exchangers through steel ducts, 4 feet 6 inches in diameter. The cool gas emerging from the heat exchangers is returned to the reactor through similar ducts in which are installed the main gas circulators or blowers. The gas circuit and blowers were designed by C. A. Parsons Ltd. In designing the circuit the firm's engineers drew on their experience with large hot-gas ducts associated with industrial gas turbines, to solve the problems arising from thrusts and expansions caused by temperature variations.

A principal consideration in blower design was the method of controlling speed. Because control of the reactor depends on the flow of gas through the core, it is necessary to be able to vary the speed of the blowers over an unusually wide range. It was therefore decided to use for the blowers a D.C. direct-drive motor controlled on the Ward-Leonard system, choosing the blower to suit this drive. The blowers had also to be designed so that carbon dioxide could not leak through their bearings from the gas ducts; a seal used in hydrogen-cooled alternators was modified to meet this requirement.

HEAT EXCHANGERS

Enough has been said about the problems of steam generation to make it clear that the heat exchangers are major components of the station. In these units gas at a pressure of 100 lb./sq. in. is passed over two water-tube boilers, one generating steam at high pressure and the other at low pressure; each boiler consists of three sections, an economizer in which the water is heated to something below boiling point, an evaporator (actually a double section) in which the water is boiled, and a superheater in which the steam from the boiling water is heated to raise its temperature. The heat exchangers were designed by Babcock and Wilcox. Each consists of a steel pressure shell 80 feet tall inside which are mounted banks of water tubes; hot gas enters through a large hole in the top of the shell, flows over the tubes, and emerges through another hole in the bottom.

It was not possible to transport complete vessels of this size to Calder Hall from the maker's works in Renfrew. The shells were therefore made in ten sections which were brought from Renfrew by road. It is amusing to find that the diameter of the finished shells was settled almost as much by the narrowest place in this road, an awkward corner in the village of Egremont, as by technical considerations.

The sections were fitted out at Renfrew with nozzles and other branches, and were stress relieved. At Calder Hall a fully equipped shop was erected in which the sections were welded together to form a complete vessel. After stress relief and testing, the vessel was dragged on a 32-wheel low-loading

13. The Turbine Hall. Above, the four 23,000 kW turbo-alternators; below, water treatment and other plant in basement of hall. In both cases this is the kind of machinery to be found in any power station.

14 (*a*). The reactor control room.

14 (*b*). The electrical (turbo-alternator) control room.

trailer to the reactor, where it was lifted upright by two 100-foot gin poles and placed in position on its plinth. Each empty shell weighed 200 tons and these lifts were the heaviest in the construction. The lifting hawsers were attached to trunnions on a steel girdle fitted round the vessel; in the first lift the girdle broke, owing to an error in design, and the vessel fell a few inches until its top was stopped by the plinth—one of the few accidents that occurred in the course of the construction. Fortunately, only trivial damage was done.

After erection, the pressure shells were fitted with their boiler tubes. The boiler tubes were made up in units consisting of vertical banks of horizontal tubes, each unit being of such a size that it could be lowered into the shell through the gas entry port at the top. Numbers of these banks were placed side by side to form the sections of the boiler. The banks were connected together by pipes taken through the wall of the shell and welded to common header tubes. By this means it was possible to restrict welding on the site to the outside of the shell; the only welds inside the shell were made in the shops under careful control. These precautions were taken to minimize the chance of leaks within the shell.

Heat transfer from gas to water was improved by, in effect, finning the boiler tubes to increase their surface area: projecting studs are electrically welded all along the tubes. These studs are streamlined to reduce the resistance to gas flow and hence minimize the pressure drop in the heat exchanger. Each heat exchanger contains about 13 miles of water tube and nearly eleven million studs.

Because any dirt inside the heat exchanger would get into the gas stream and hence the reactor, the pressure shell and all its boiler tubes had to be scrupulously clean inside. The tubes and other fittings were therefore installed in clean conditions similar to those imposed when laying graphite.

Although the boilers have been designed to reduce to a minimum the chances of a leak between steam and gas, it has

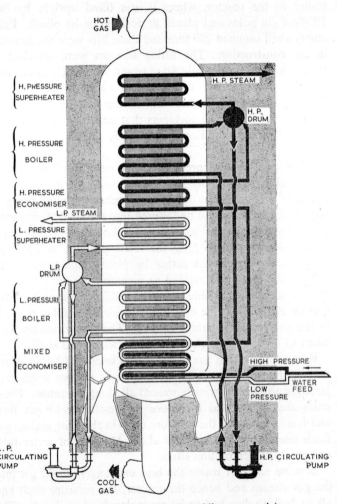

Figure 8.   The heat exchanger (diagrammatic).

not been possible to guarantee that this will never occur. Means have therefore been provided to deal with any leaks that might develop. Leakage of water into the gas would be shown by humidity indicators in the gas circuit. The faulty heat exchanger would then be shut off on both gas and steam sides and emptied of water; gas remaining in the pressure shell would leak through the faulty tube and enable it to be identified and cut out of circuit by welding on caps outside the shell. All these operations could be carried out without entering the clean shell.

THE TURBINE HALL

The steam from the heat exchangers is fed to two turbo-electric generators. Each turbine is really two machines in one, a high-pressure machine coupled to a low-pressure one. Compared with turbines in coal-fired power stations, these machines are fed with low-quality steam—even on the high-pressure side the pressure is only 200 lb./sq. in. and there is an unusually large quantity of low-pressure steam. The machines have consequently been designed with large exhausts and special care has been necessary to reduce the effects of wet steam on the blades of the low-pressure turbine. The turbo-alternators are supported on reinforced concrete blocks of complicated shape, with tunnels for steam pipes and cornices supporting auxiliaries. The blocks were made in a single pour of concrete by a specially devised technique. Each of the four alternators is capable of generating 23,000 kW of electricity, giving a total maximum output of 92,000 kW; part of this is used to supply the factory, but a net output of 60,000 to 65,000 kW is available for the national grid.

Ancillary equipment in the turbine hall includes the turbine exhaust condensers, the dump condensers, equipment for removing air and mineral impurities from the feed water to the boilers—the de-aeration plant and the de-mineralizing plant—and the carbon dioxide plant. The carbon dioxide is stored as a liquid in tanks under pressure and is evaporated

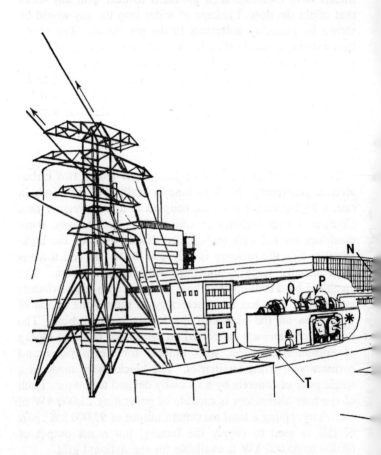

A DIAGRAMMATIC VIE

A. Pressure Vessel; B. Biological Shield (Concrete); C. Ther
Bricks; F. Hot Gas Outlet; G. Control Rods; H. Charging Tub
Exchanger; N. Steampipe to Turbine; O. Cool Gas Outlet; P. Ste
Chimney; T. Cable Duct to Transformers; X. Gap

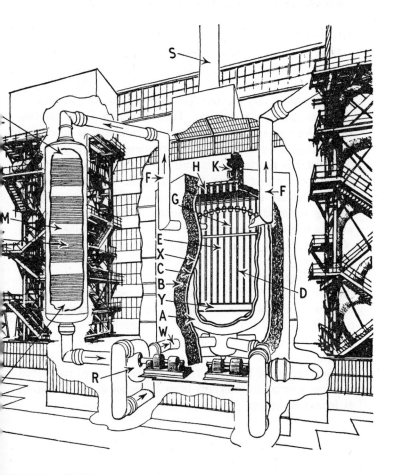

CALDER HALL

...eld (Steel); D. Uranium Fuel Elements; E. Graphite Moderator
...Charge/Discharge Machine; L. Hot Gas Inlet; M. Heat
...bine; Q. Alternator; R. Gas Circulating Fans; S. Cooling Air
...oling Air; Y. Diagrid; Z. Water Tubes; * Condenser.

in steam-heated boilers when wanted for the reactor. There are nearly 26 tons of gas in the complete gas circuit.

THE COOLING TOWERS

It is a curious fact that, from a distance, the most conspicuous objects at Calder Hall are the least unorthodox parts of the plant. They are the diabolo-shaped concrete cooling towers and are familiar to everyone who has seen a conventional power station. Their function is as follows. Steam, for example, from the turbine exhausts, is condensed by passing it over tubes (in the condensers) through which cold water is flowing. This water is warmed in doing its job and, in order that it can be used again, it is taken to the cooling towers to be cooled. Incidentally the quantity of cooling water is very large. Nearly 150,000,000 gallons of water a day circulate round the plant; about 3,000,000 gallons of this are lost by evaporation and have to be made up from the rivers.

A cooling tower is simply a large chimney built over a shallow pond. Warm water from the condensers is led into the tower near its base and allowed to fall in a spray into the pond; as it falls it is cooled by the current of air which is forced by convection to rise through the chimney. The cooling towers at Calder Hall are 300 feet high and 190 feet in diameter at the bottom. The shells are made of reinforced concrete varying in thickness from 16 inches at the bottom to $4\frac{1}{2}$ inches at the top.

CHAPTER FOUR

Reactor No. 1 Starts Up

The first reactor was completed (apart from charging it with fuel elements) in the middle of May 1956. The whole plant consists of two reactors with their associated heat exchangers, a turbine hall, and two cooling towers. The plant is called Calder Hall A and a copy of it, Calder Hall B, is being built alongside and within the same fence. Thus the complete factory will consist of four reactors and their associated plant. All these reactors will be dual-purpose plants; between them they will be feeding nearly 150 MW of electrical power into the grid, enough to supply the domestic needs of a city of a million people, at the same time as they are making plutonium. The decision to add this second pair of reactors was announced by the Minister of Fuel and Power in the House of Commons on 13 June 1955. He also announced that four other reactors, for the same purpose and of the same type, would be built at some other site. This site has been fixed at Chapel Cross near Annan in Dumfriesshire; the plant there will be a copy of Calder Hall, laid out a little differently.

OPERATIONS

The responsibility for charging the reactor and starting it up (and of course for its subsequent operations) belongs to the Operations Branch of the Industrial Group. In the early stages of design the engineers of this section were called upon principally for advice on operational aspects, on such matters as what layout would be convenient, what arrangement of controls would be most efficient, what instruments would be needed in operation, what health monitors were needed. As design and construction advanced the operations engineers played a greater and greater part. They did inspections of parts of the plant as they were taken over from contractors, and also full-scale engineering inspection of critical work such as graphite laying. They also ensured not only that operating requirements were met but also that the engineers were familiar with details of equipment before they took it into their charge. Operations engineers worked out procedures for start-up and operation and wrote detailed operating instructions to be used by the staff when the factory was commissioned; in this task they drew heavily upon their experience with the Windscale piles.

The Operations Branch is also responsible for safety of the plant, by giving advice at the design stage, checking equipment installed, drawing up procedures to be observed especially in monitoring for radioactivity, and training personnel. The record of AEA factories shows that the atomic energy industry is extremely safe—lost time from sickness and accidents compares favourably with other industries—and every care is taken to maintain and improve this record. Some of the operations at a station like Calder Hall involve hazards not present in conventional factories, owing to the presence of radioactivity, but the nature of these hazards is well understood and unpleasant consequences can be avoided by proper monitoring and routine.

It cannot be too strongly emphasized that there is no possibility of an 'atomic explosion' taking place in a power reactor. The worst that could happen would be no more dangerous than accidents in many other industries. And the chances of accident at Calder Hall are remote—as has been said earlier, it is a very safe plant.

START-UP

The Operations Branch is also responsible for loading and starting up the Authority's production reactors. A nuclear fire is not started by piling lumps of fuel above a fire-lighter and applying a match. In the first place, as was explained in Chapter 1, a nuclear fire cannot burn until a certain minimum critical amount of fuel has been brought together—a chain fission reaction will sustain itself only when the assembly of fuel and moderator has reached (or exceeded) the critical size. Then once this critical size has been reached, the fire starts by itself—sufficient neutrons are released in spontaneous fission to trigger the reaction and there is no need for the operator to apply the equivalent of a match to the fuel. The critical size depends on the neutron economy of the core and the factors that affect it, particularly the purity and neutron absorption of materials. Because some of these factors are not known with complete certainty, or may vary rather considerably, the calculated value of the critical size is likely to differ somewhat from the actual value. For this reason a reactor is loaded in small increments until the critical size is reached.

Reactor No. 1 at Calder Hall, empty of fuel but otherwise complete, was handed over by the Engineering Branch to the Operations Branch on the evening 17 May 1956 and loading began at once. The fuel elements, after inspection, were placed in the charging machine at the top of the reactor. Then, with the pressure vessel open to the atmosphere, the elements were loaded into the channels in the graphite core, beginning at the centre. At the same time a close watch was kept on the neutron population, as shown by the low-level power-measuring instruments. During the first stages, uranium was added in quite large quantities, a ton or so at a time, but as the expected critical size was approached these quantities were reduced until during the last stages elements were put in one by one and the instruments studied with growing expectation as each element went in. For most of this time the effect of each addition of uranium was to cause the neutron population to increase a little and then become constant. But at 7.15 p.m. on 22 May the critical rod went in and the watching engineers saw the needle of the period meter climb slowly and then remain steady, instead of sinking back, indicating that the neutron population was growing steadily. The chain reaction had started—the pile had become 'divergent'.

With divergency established, the control rods were put in and the reactor shut down, though its power had not exceeded a thousandth of a watt up to this stage. Comparison of the loading at divergency with the calculated loading showed that the critical size was smaller than calculated, indicating that the neutron economy of the core was considerably better than the design value. This meant that there would be spare reactivity which would be useful in operation later on. The loading was then continued, until early in June the full complement of uranium rods had been put in the core. At Calder Hall the loading procedure was based on that used for the Windscale piles and the latter experience, combined with greater confidence about the critical mass, enabled the loading to be completed quickly.

WORKING-UP

A long process of working-up followed divergence and the completion of loading. First the control rods were calibrated so that the operator would know exactly how much reactivity would be absorbed or released by a given movement of the rods. In making this calibration, advantage was taken of the fact that the reactivity of a reactor is very sensitive to changes in the pressure of air in the core; increasing the air pressure causes the concentration of neutron-absorbing nitrogen atoms to increase and hence the reactivity to decrease. The rods were calibrated by closing the pressure vessel and pumping in air up to the full gas pressure of 100 lb./sq. in. at which the reactor would ultimately work, noting the effect of the control rods on reactivity at different intermediate pressures. There then followed trials with the charge/discharge gear and after this the power was allowed to rise to about 1000 kW, still with air only in the core. At this low power the gear for detecting faulty fuel elements was calibrated, by putting small pieces of bare uranium into the core and noting their effect on the detecting instruments.

With these trials completed, the pressure vessel was closed

and it and the gas circuits were emptied of air by means of vacuum pumps and then purged by filling them several times with carbon dioxide gas at atmospheric pressure. Then the system was filled with the full charge of gas and the blowers, valves, and other parts of the gas circuit, tested under various conditions. After this the reactor power was gradually raised over a period of weeks, and further checks made; the gas was heated and steam generated until finally live steam was fed first to the dump condenser and then to the turbines. The final step in commissioning sees the turbines run up and electric power generated by the alternators, the output increasing as the design temperature of the reactor is approached. With all the many checks and measurements that were essential it is not surprising that nearly six months will elapse between divergence and full power output.

Needless to say, working-up and operation present many problems, some unexpected. These cannot be discussed here but it may be worth mentioning one instance in which trouble was anticipated by the provision of equipment to deal with it, though so far the equipment has not been needed. It will have been realized that charging and discharging fuel elements is rather like fishing in muddy water; the operator cannot see the thing he is trying to lift, he can only feel it through his machine. When the designers considered also the damage that radiation may do to a fuel element, it seemed to them that sooner or later something would go wrong in this operation—a grab might break and drop a cartridge or a hauling wire might fail. They have therefore fitted shock-absorbers at the bottoms of the channels and provided a number of cunning contrivances to enable broken parts to be removed. A very small television camera has been developed with which a channel may be inspected throughout its length.

Television had already played a part in connexion with the Windscale piles, where it was used to inspect the front and back faces. On the basis of the information obtained repairs were carried out in spite of the high degree of radioactivity.

The development by the factory staff of methods for doing repairs in active areas has had another effect on Calder Hall. Because the operations engineers could do this, they were able to increase considerably the through-put of the Windscale chemical plant, in which plutonium is extracted from irradiated uranium. This increase has been great enough to enable the plant to handle uranium from Calder Hall as well as from Windscale, so it has not been necessary to build another chemical plant

CHAPTER FIVE

Answers for the Engineers: The Role of Research

The theoretical and experimental research done for the feasibility study at Harwell had enabled an estimate to be made of the seriousness of the various problems and had shown in broad terms how the latter might be solved. But there is a wide gap between broad solutions of this kind and detailed designs for components or factory processes, for example between showing what canning materials are permissible in a fuel element and designing a fuel element that can be produced in quantity in a factory.

Consequently a great deal of research and development remained to be done after the completion of the feasibility study and during the actual construction of the factory. Preliminary results had to be confirmed and extended where possible on a scale more nearly that of the complete reactor; detail had to be filled in; factory processes devised and tested. Some of the work was done at Harwell but detailed development of this kind is primarily the responsibility of the Research and Development Branch of the Industrial Group. This branch has to find answers to problems arising in the course of design, and its work is tied to target dates in the same rigorous way as the work of the design offices. The design engineers go ahead with their projects on the assumption that they will get their answers by the time that they need them; at the same time as construction people are digging holes and putting up buildings, the equipment that is to go into those buildings is the subject of research by Research and Development Branch. There can be few other organizations in which design is so close on the heels of development as it is at Risley.

FUEL ELEMENT

The biggest single item of development work was that done for the fuel element. Nearly half a million pounds were spent in establishing a design and a production line on which the element could be manufactured. As in all work of this kind, time pressed. A stock of many thousands of fuel elements would be needed when the reactor was ready for loading; these would take perhaps six months to produce; before this production began, the operations people wanted several months in which to work up the production line; design of the line would take at least another six months; so the information needed for designing the line would be wanted almost as soon as the outline of the reactor design had been settled.

The feasibility study had recommended a fuel element consisting of a 4-foot-long uranium rod, about an inch in diameter, enclosed in a can made from a magnesium alloy of a new type; the can was to be fitted with fins of a specified type. It was now necessary to confirm that the materials proposed were compatible with the carbon dioxide coolant in all conditions likely to occur in operation, that the heat transfer properties were satisfactory, and that the cartridges could be made in quantity to the specifications; fabrication methods for the uranium rods had to be established and it had to be shown that the rods would behave themselves in operation, and not become distorted by the action of heat or radiation during their expected operating lifetime.

The original experiments at Harwell had shown that, of the series of magnesium alloys developed, the one called Magnox E was most resistant to corrosion in general and was therefore recommended for Pippa. However, when it came to making a can, this material turned out to be difficult to weld, but another member of the series, Magnox C, was satisfactory and also was as resistant as Magnox E to corrosion and oxidation in the now-specified Pippa conditions. Magnox C on the other hand had not been tested as thoroughly as

Magnox E; Research and Development Branch had therefore to investigate its behaviour over a wide range of conditions. These investigations showed among other things that the alloy must be extremely free from traces of contaminating metals if there was to be no possibility of rapid reactions and consequent failure at high temperature. One accidental demonstration of the importance of slight contamination was given when some cans were being heated in carbon dioxide; several experiments had been made without event and then three of four cartridges failed suddenly, part of the can melting at temperatures much lower than expected from earlier experiments. Ultimately it was found that the uranium rods in these cartridges had been straightened by hammering them with a lead, instead of hard-rubber, hammer and that specks of lead had stuck to the uranium. This lead formed an alloy with the Magnox which melted at a comparatively low temperature and so caused a puncture in the can.

This discovery showed that it would be necessary to test all possible contaminants that might be picked up in the course of manufacture, and a long series of experiments began. Copper, aluminium, lead, and several other common metals were found to give rise to similar troubles, though fortunately iron turned out to be compatible with Magnox. These results necessitated considerable changes in the design of the canning lines and in factory inspection, to ensure that completed cartridges should not fail in service. Many commonly used metals had to be rigorously excluded from the factory and this necessity affected incidental operations. For example, electricians could not solder wires in the usual way because the copper bits of their soldering irons and the lead-tin alloy of their solder would introduce forbidden metals into the shop.

This example illustrates the kind of problem that the development scientist has to solve; he has to keep his eye not only on the materials and processes of primary interest but also on a host of minor matters quite remotely connected with the erection of machinery or the routine of factory management. Thus the temperature of a factory making Magnox cans could not be measured by ordinary mercury-in-glass thermometers in case one was broken, because mercury is a particularly undesirable contaminant.

Further minor adjustments to the alloy were necessary and these experiments took a long time, because for each change samples of the new alloy had to be made in half-ton lots. With the constitution of the alloy settled, the next step was to find a way of manufacturing sound billets of the required purity, on a factory scale. Soundness in the billets involved care in casting and control of grain size; purity necessitated extreme cleanliness in all operations and ancillary processes. Factory methods to achieve these ends were developed by the manufacturers working in collaboration with Research and Development Branch.

Having established a technique for manufacturing satisfactory billets of the alloy, the next problem was to produce from them finned cans of the required size. The dimensions had to be kept within close limits and the surface had to be very smooth and clean. Again much development was necessary by the manufacturers, advised by Research and Development Branch. This work is by no means finished because the process now used is expensive, involving as it does machining from solid bar, and a cheaper and more efficient method is being sought.

In the reactor the fuel elements rest one upon the other in the vertical channels, alignment being ensured by means of cone joints at each end of an element. It is clearly essential that the fuel elements be as straight as possible before insertion in the reactor, and shall become as little bowed as possible during operation, despite the considerable stresses set up in the lower ones by the vertical stacking, or they might jam in the channels and make discharging difficult. As one precaution against bowing, the fuel element was shortened from the 4 feet originally proposed to 3 feet 4 inches.

15. Shell of a heat exchanger before erection.

16. The electricity produced is fed into the 'grid'.

Shorter elements than this would have meant so many more to the channel that charging and discharging would take an unacceptably long time; there would also have been a loss in reactivity.

Metallurgical means of improving the strength of the uranium rods, and of reducing the effects of operation, were also sought. Heating and cooling and neutron irradiation produce bowing by a mechanism similar to that which causes the surface of a uranium rod to wrinkle. Research at Harwell during the feasibility study had shown that wrinkling was prevented if the uranium metal contained no large grains, so an industrial method had to be found for making fine-grained uranium. It was finally recommended by the Research and Development Branch that the uranium rods should be passed through a high-frequency heating coil into a cooling spray. The method works very well but the experiments illustrate some of the difficulties under which work of this kind is done. It takes a long time to develop and manufacture the special high-frequency generators and furnaces needed, and so this expensive equipment had to be ordered for the production line before the experiments had been completed and the desirability of the treatment confirmed. The act of faith has been justified by the event; the treatment produces the desired fine grain and the rods are satisfactorily straight.

Having made a good can and a good uranium rod the next thing is to make sure that the can remains a good fit on the rod during the whole of its operating life. The trouble here arises from the fact that magnesium expands on heating (and contracts on cooling) twice as much as uranium. Consequently when the fuel element is heated the can lengthens beyond the uranium and on cooling collapses on to it and a bit of the can is, as it were, left behind with no uranium in it; if heating and cooling is repeated several times the can may ultimately fail. The process can be compared with the process of working a sock off one's foot by rubbing the stockinged foot on a carpeted floor several times. It is called ratchetting. A method of preventing ratchetting was developed at Harwell during the feasibility study but again the Research and Development Branch had to do a considerable amount of development to establish a satisfactory factory process.

Finally a test and inspection procedure had to be worked out. Dimensional checks were straightforward but some difficulty was experienced in finding a satisfactory method for ensuring that there were no leaks in the cans, particularly from the welded joints. As a guide to future design the manufacturing history, including test observations, for every one of the tens of thousands of fuel elements made for the reactors is recorded on punched cards so that statistical studies of the different aspects of manufacture can be made with the least amount of difficulty.

Whilst the factory canning line was being built, the Research and Development Branch began a small-scale production run on their experimental canning line to test the procedures and provide a supply of cartridges for tests. A hundred or so cartridges were made in this way, and this apparently expensive operation has more than justified itself in getting the production line going.

COOLANT COMPATIBILITY

As we saw in Chapter 2, a crucial set of measurements during the feasibility study was that made at Harwell on the reaction between graphite and carbon dioxide. The results gave confidence in the choice of this gas, but the measurements still left a number of unresolved questions and it was considered necessary to extend the observations to conditions more nearly representative of those that would exist in the reactor. It was therefore decided to build in the Harwell experimental pile, Bepo, a full-sized replica of one of the channels for the Calder Hall reactor.

This channel consisted of a stainless steel tube, 48 feet long, running horizontally right through the core of Bepo. Inside this tube were placed, end to end, tubes of graphite so as to form a continuous channel of the right diameter, and in the central hole of which canned uranium fuel elements rested. Carbon dioxide was circulated through the channel (by means of a blower) through filters, a meter, and a heater, these parts of the circuit being outside the reactor. By proper adjustment of the blower speed and heater input the pressure and temperature of the gas could be made the same as that expected in the Calder Hall reactor. Arrangements were made to analyse the gas and so determine the rate at which carbon monoxide was formed and its equilibrium concentration. It was also possible to remove graphite samples from time to time and find out whether there were any changes in weight. On the downstream side of the gas outlet, samples of steel were placed to observe the effects on steel used for the pressure vessel.

This elaborate arrangement, which is called a pile loop, is typical of the kind of experiment which has to be done when information is needed about the behaviour of a system or material under irradiation. This particular loop gave quite a good approximation to conditions in the Calder Hall reactor except in one important respect; the neutron flux available in Bepo is considerably smaller than it will be at Calder. Since irradiation effects are generally proportional to the total dose of neutrons, a reduction in neutron flux means longer exposure to achieve a given dose and so experiments in Bepo take a long time. The new reactor Dido, which has recently come into operation at Harwell, has a much higher flux than Bepo and shortens considerably the time needed for some of these vitally important experiments.

The Pippa loop in Bepo provided much-needed information about the graphite reaction with carbon dioxide and a long series of experiments has been made. This work is being continued to extend the results to conditions likely to be met in future gas-cooled reactors.

HEAT TRANSFER

The experiments made during the feasibility study on the transfer of heat from a circumferentially-finned can had established the general suitability of this type for the power-producing reactor. In these experiments, however, the coolant had been air at atmospheric pressure. Conditions in the Calder Hall reactor would be considerably different from this. The density of the gas would be different. the pressure would be seven times as great, and the mass flow (the mass of gas pumped along the channel in unit time) would be increased. These changes meant that the turbulence of the gas as it flowed down the channel would be different, and this would affect the heat transfer and resistance to flow. Moreover since the greater mass flow would remove heat from the fins more quickly, the power of the fins to conduct heat was important; if heat flowed down the fins only slowly, it would not reach the tips and so part of the fins would be wasted. It was therefore necessary to study the properties of fins made of metals having different heat conductivities. Had the cans not been finned, but been simply plain cylinders, it would have been possible to calculate their performance in the changed conditions, but the behaviour of finned surfaces is too complicated for this. Further complications were introduced by the method of supporting the cartridges in their vertical channels.

A set of experiments had therefore to be made under conditions similar to those that would exist in the reactor. For this purpose a vertical channel was built of the same size, through which carbon dioxide could be blown at the same pressure, as in Pippa. Models of fuel elements were put in the channel and the heat lost from them measured under various conditions. It was not necessary to build this loop in the Harwell pile, since heat transfer is not affected by radiation. A comprehensive series of measurements has been made in this rig and this series has been supplemented by measurements at Windscale, particularly with cans taken from the prototype canning production line.

NUCLEAR CALCULATIONS AND EXPERIMENTS

The development of fuel elements involved principally experiments in metallurgy, chemistry, and engineering. Another group of calculations and experiments was concerned with the nuclear physics of the reacting core. For the feasibility study the critical size of the core had been worked out assuming certain lattice spacings, rod diameters, and neutron absorption in graphite, uranium, and magnesium. Many of these assumed values were uncertain, however, so the calculations had been necessarily approximate. For design purposes a more elaborate and refined set of calculations was needed.

These fresh calculations, which were done by Research and Development Branch, were made in two steps. In the first, the object was to work out, approximately, the best core in terms of the concentration of fissile uranium atoms in the fuel metal, that is, of the enrichment of the uranium. The physicists chose a range of values for lattice spacing and rod diameter, and calculated, for various points in this range, the uranium enrichment needed to provide the required reactivity in the core; from the results it was possible to pick a lattice and rod size that would give the most reactivity for the least enrichment, i.e. for natural uranium. Having done this, definitive core calculations were made to take account of the detailed design of the graphite structure, including the various holes and cracks left between blocks for structural reasons, and to provide estimates of the reactivity that would be available under various conditions of operation, such. for example, as operation at high temperature. These calculations also covered the effects of poisoning, that is of the absorption of neutrons by fission products that grow, in the radioactive sense, when a reactor is shut down. Having grown, these poisons decay by transformation to other elements which have smaller neutron-absorbing powers and so their effect is not permanent, but there is a period of a few hours after a reactor is shut down, during which considerably more reactivity (i.e. considerably more spare neutrons) is needed to make it start than is necessary after standing for some time or during operation. It is important to know how great this poisoning effect will be so that the core can be designed with a sufficient margin of reactivity to enable the reactor to be restarted quickly after shut-down.

The effect of the control rods had also to be worked out to make sure that they would be able to absorb all the reactivity required in all circumstances. These calculations were complicated by the fact that the rods are disposed asymmetrically, inasmuch as all enter from one end of the core, and some ingenious mathematical tricks were devised to overcome the difficulties. The answers gave an essentially static picture of the performance of the control rods, a calibration curve which indicated the reactivity at selected settings of the rods. It was desirable to supplement this with a more dynamic estimate and for this purpose an electronic analogue computer—a so-called electronic brain—developed at Harwell was used to calculate continuously the performance under given operating conditions.

In spite of all this mathematical skill, these calculations gave results that were still uncertain because the data upon which they were based were not always known accurately, particularly the critical neutron-absorbing powers of materials used. These uncertainties reflect the difficulties of making accurate measurements in nuclear physics, difficulties that arise partly in the techniques of measurements and partly in preparing isotopically-pure samples of the materials.

Calculations based on the properties of the individual materials in the reactor core had therefore to be supplemented by an experiment in which the whole assembly was observed working together, an integral experiment. The obvious integral experiment would be to build the proposed reactor and see whether it worked, but clearly this would be impracticable. A so-called exponential experiment or sub-critical experiment, was made therefore. A pile of graphite bricks was built into a cube about 10 feet on a side in the configuration proposed for the reactor, with channels and other voids, and loaded with uranium cartridges. This pile is much too small for a self-sustaining chain reaction to be set up. Sources of neutrons were then placed under the pile, causing neutrons to stream through it; some of these neutrons cause fissions and so there is some multiplication but not enough to cause a self-sustaining chain reaction. Instead the neutron density dies out exponentially towards the edges of the pile, but within the pile the neutrons are distributed in the same manner as they would be in a full-sized reactor and by measuring the neutron population at different points in the pile the performance of the reactor can be forecast quite closely.

These experiments for Calder Hall were made at Harwell in an exponential pile so designed as to enable measurements to be made with different lattice arrangements and channel diameters and various uranium enrichments. The results provided the final assurance the designers needed that their finished reactor would work with natural uranium. In fact, as we have seen, there was some reactivity to spare.

CHAPTER SIX

Nuclear Power: The Future

It is only to be expected that electricity generated at Calder Hall will cost more than electricity generated in an up-to-date coal-fired station. Calder Hall is a prototype; for this reason alone construction costs are high and hence a high figure for amortization of capital charges must appear in the price of electricity generated. Moreover, the plant has been designed as a dual-purpose plant, to produce plutonium for military purposes as well as electric power; it follows, for reasons already given, that as a power generator its efficiency is not as good as could be achieved. However, it is confidently believed that in gas-cooled reactors built primarily to produce power and embodying improvements already seen to be practicable, electricity generated will not cost more than $0.6d.$ per unit. This figure of $0.6d.$ takes account of the plutonium produced by including a credit based on a reasonable, but cautious, estimate of the value of plutonium as a fuel for civil reactors. With further improvements which experience will undoubtedly show to be practicable, it is likely that the cost will go lower still.

IMPROVEMENTS IN GAS-COOLED REACTORS

The Calder Hall reactors have been compared, perhaps slightingly, with the Model T Ford car and the reciprocating steam engine, but it must be remembered that both of these were major engineering achievements which permanently affected industrial developments. Gas-cooled reactors will surely leave a similar mark. Because they unquestionably have a future it is worth considering briefly the direction in which they are likely to be developed.

As will be apparent from early chapters, the design of the Calder Hall reactors depended in many places on

extrapolations from known engineering practice. These extrapolations were often cautious because the designers felt
obliged to avoid taking chances either with the successful
operation of the plant or, especially, with the possibility of
accidents. Experience has already shown where this caution
has been excessive and hence where improvements in performance or reduction in costs can be made.

The capital cost of a unit of electricity sent out would be
reduced if the total heat generated in the reactor could be
increased for a less-than-proportionate increase in cost of
plant. One way to do this would be to increase the size of the
core but then a larger pressure vessel would be needed. At
Calder Hall the size of the pressure vessel was decided by the
thickness of steel plate which could be welded on site. With
the experience now available the designers feel confident that
considerably thicker plate could be used, possibly as much as
3 inches, and therefore that larger pressure vessels could be
built in the immediate future. Alternatively, higher pressure
gas might be used in a pressure vessel of the same size.

Considerable advantages could be gained by improving the
thermal properties of the reactor, particularly by increasing
the heat rating (that is the amount of heat generated for unit
mass of fuel in the core) and the temperature at which the
heat is removed. Better transfer of heat from the fuel element
would increase heat rating at once. This might be achieved by
adopting better fins or even by using radically different fuel
elements, perhaps tubes or flat plates instead of solid rods.
Much more research into the heat-transfer properties of
different fins is needed and much more detailed assessment
of the nuclear properties of differently shaped fuel elements.
By increasing gas pressure, more heat could be extracted for
a given blower power (or alternatively a lower blower power
would be required for a given heat output) but this would
require a thicker pressure vessel. A major change that might
be possible would be to use a gas with better heat-transfer
properties than carbon dioxide.

Increasing the temperature of operation would pay big dividends. It would not only lead to an increase in the efficiency of the steam side but also it would enable the size of the turbines and their associated gear to be reduced. Part of the high capital cost of Calder Hall arises from the fact that the comparatively poor-quality steam has necessitated the use of turbines large compared with those in modern conventional stations. Increased pressure does, however, bring up a number of problems. The pressure vessel would have to operate at higher temperature and this would necessitate the use of creep-resistant steels, which are hard to weld. Above all, high temperature means changes in the fuel element cans. Better magnesium alloys may be forthcoming but for a really major improvement in temperature other metals will have to be used, perhaps zirconium or beryllium.

There are thus many possibilities for upgrading the performance of gas-cooled reactors. Even if the more radical changes are ignored and only the modifications immediately practicable were adopted, it seems likely that the electrical output could be increased three or four times without adding more than 10 or 15 per cent to the cost of construction. Further developments should lead to even better performance and lower costs. Just as the reciprocating steam engine was improved upon as the years passed, so the gas-cooled pile may well be streamlined and therefore made more economical, and it will certainly give valuable service for a period comparable, on the shortened time-scale of this fast-moving age, with the two hundred years for which the steam engine has held its own. At any rate confidence in the gas-cooled reactor is sufficiently great to make it the basis of the first stage of the ten-year programme for nuclear power in the United Kingdom.

THE TEN-YEAR NUCLEAR POWER PROGRAMME

This programme was announced in a White Paper published in February 1955. It covers the ten years from 1955 to 1965, by the end of which period it is expected that nuclear power will be contributing 1500 to 2000 MW of electricity to the grid and replacing five to six million tons of coal a year by a few hundred tons of uranium. The estimated cost of this programme is £300,000,000; this figure includes the cost of additions to ancillary plant including plant for manufacturing fuel elements and processing plant for spent fuel. Beyond 1965 the White Paper does not attempt more than an indication of the way in which nuclear power might develop—technical uncertainties are too great to permit any more positive statements—but if all goes well it is hoped that by 1975 nuclear power will provide a total generating capacity of 10,000 to 15,000 MW (replacing 40,000,000 tons of coal a year) and that by then all the new generating capacity required each year, estimated at 3000 MW, would be provided by nuclear power stations. It should be noted that the Calder Hall and Chapel Cross stations are not regarded as forming part of this programme and their electrical output is not included in the figures given.

The ten-year programme calls for the construction of twelve nuclear power stations. The first three stations, which form stage I of the programme, will each have two gas-cooled reactors of a design basically that of Calder Hall but improved along the lines just sketched, so as to give several times the electrical output. For stage II of the programme it is expected that more highly rated reactors will have been developed; consequently only one should be needed for each station. These reactors may be liquid- rather than gas-cooled in order to achieve the desired increase in rating, though one cannot rule out the possibility that major improvements in gas cooling may be forthcoming. Two types of liquid-cooled reactors are being studied. In the first, ordinary water at high pressure is used both as moderator and as coolant. In the second the moderator is graphite and the coolant liquid sodium. The fuel used in these stage II reactors will probably be enriched with the plutonium produced in stage I reactors.

It is unlikely that the reactors in these stations will burn more than a small proportion of the fissile atoms in the uranium fuel—their utilization or burn-up will be low. In stage I reactors it is expected that burn-up will be such that 1 ton of uranium will be equivalent to 10,000 tons of coal. These reactors will, however, also produce plutonium, which can be used as fuel in later reactors. In stage II reactors, which will burn plutonium, it is hoped that as much as 30,000 tons of coal equivalent will be reached. Attainment of burn-up approaching the theoretical equivalent of 3,000,000 tons of coal to 1 ton of uranium must await the development of breeder reactors, i.e. reactors which produce more of a secondary fuel than they burn of primary fuel. These are expected after 1965 in what is sometimes spoken of as stage III of the programme.

Several types of breeder are being examined. The first is the fast reactor, sometimes likened to the gas turbine of the nuclear age. No moderator is used and highly-enriched fuel is necessary. In its final form the reactor will have a core of plutonium rods surrounded by a blanket of uranium metal. Heat will be removed by liquid sodium and used to raise steam. Neutrons escaping from the core will enter the blanket and there transmute uranium-238 to plutonium. Experiments at Harwell in the zero-energy plutonium reactor Zephyr have shown that in a full-scale fast reactor, for each plutonium atom undergoing fission in the core, 1·7 fresh atoms will be produced in the blanket. To the physicist, therefore, the reactor is a good breeder, but to the engineer, metallurgist, and chemist it is a blinding headache. An enormous amount of heat has to be extracted from a small volume—100 MW generated in a core the size of a dustbin—and this means major difficulties in heat transfer, in stability of components under extraordinary thermal gradients, and in the damage caused by irradiation. The fuel and blanket materials have to be processed many times in the course of their lives in order to recover the newly-bred fuel; this means that chemists and metallurgists must devise recovery processes far cheaper than those at present used, otherwise the cost of recovered fuel will be so inflated by processing charges that it will represent not a credit but a debit and so power generation would be uneconomic. Nevertheless these problems are being intensively investigated. A large-scale experimental fast reactor is being built at Dounreay, in the north of Scotland, to develop 60 MW of heat. The nuclear performance of this system is being studied at Harwell in Zeus, a zero-energy fast reactor fuelled with uranium-235.

The classic graphite-moderated thermal reactor cannot be used for breeding because its neutron economy is too poor, but there are varieties of thermal reactor, among them the aqueous homogeneous type, which would have a sufficient surplus of neutrons to permit breeding. The aqueous homogeneous reactor differs from the reactors so far described in that the uranium fuel and water moderator are combined in a solution of uranyl sulphate in light (or heavy) water. The core is in fact a soup instead of a plum pudding. As in the fast reactor, the core will be surrounded by a blanket of fertile material in which new fuel will be bred; probably this blanket will be made of thorium rather than uranium so the newly bred fuel will be uranium-233 and not plutonium. The fuel atoms in the soup may be uranium-233, when it is available, or uranium-235.

This type of reactor has many attractive qualities. Radioactive waste products, particularly fission product gases, could be removed continuously from the core solution, thus reducing the absorption of neutrons and so helping to breed. The absence of metallic fuel elements means that distortion and similar difficulties caused by radiation damage would be eliminated. It might even be possible to pump the soup through a heat exchanger and make it act as its own coolant. Inevitably, however, there is a price for these advantages. The hot radioactive core solution is corrosive, so searching experiments are necessary to find a suitable material for the core vessel. A continuous process to remove fission products is easier to devise in principle than to engineer in practice. Nevertheless the difficulties will undoubtedly be overcome. A considerable programme of experimental work is going ahead at Harwell and a zero-energy homogeneous reactor, Zetr, has been operating there since the beginning of 1956.

INDUSTRIAL PARTICIPATION IN THE POWER PROGRAMME

It is important to note that the stations projected in the White Paper programme will be built, not by the Atomic Energy Authority, but by private industry for the Electricity Authorities, who will own and operate them. This is of course similar to the existing practice in the construction of coal-fired stations. As the only body with experience in the field, the Atomic Energy Authority's part in the programme is to give technical advice on the nuclear plant and to help in training the staff of industrial firms, of consulting engineers, and of the Electricity Authorities. In later stages of development, when industry has acquired experience, the Authority, whilst continuing to give such help as may be needed, will remain (apart from its activities in the military field) primarily a research and development organization and will continue to do long-term research and to design, build, and operate pioneering types of power reactors. The Authority will also be responsible for buying uranium, for fabricating fuel elements, and for processing used fuel and blanket materials and extracting plutonium or uranium-233 from them.

The power programme is in fact backed by extensive collaboration between the Atomic Energy Authority on the one hand and industry and the Electricity Authorities on the other. Various firms have from time to time had the chance to acquire experience in the atomic energy field through contracts for parts of the Calder Hall or other reactors, but up to two years ago industry was given no general view of nuclear power development. When the building of Calder

Hall began, however, the Authority lost no time in passing their experience to industry and a considerable number of engineers from firms were attached to Harwell, to work alongside the Establishment's staff on various projects. In the early summer of 1954 this collaboration was taken a step further when twenty-five attached staff attended a three-month trial course of formal instruction in the fundamentals of nuclear reactors, at the newly formed Harwell Reactor School. This Reactor School now runs regular courses which are open to students from all over the world. The Industrial Group also runs a scheme in which engineers from industry are given experience at Risley and in the factories. Towards the end of 1956 this scheme will be extended by the opening of a Reactor Operation School at Calder Hall; this school will use the factory's reactors to provide advanced instruction in the problems of reactor operation, for engineers who have been through the Harwell Reactor School or are otherwise suitably qualified. By these means industrial engineers are being given a very thorough and comprehensive acquaintance with atomic energy methods and problems.

In the autumn of 1954 industrial firms set up four groups to study the design of nuclear power plants. Each group was led by a manufacturer of heavy electrical machinery and included a boilermaker and other specialists. The immediate aim of these firms is to design improved Calder Hall type reactors for the power programme. Basic information comes generally from the AEA and is of course freely interchanged between the groups of firms, but in design matters the groups are competitors for orders from the Electricity Authorities for nuclear power stations. Construction of the first station is to begin in the spring of 1957.

It should be emphasized that the nuclear power stations of the ten-year programme are for civil use only and all the plutonium produced in them will be available to fuel the civil reactors in stage II. The civil programme in fact is in no way dependent on selling plutonium to military customers. On the other hand it would be wrong to pretend that the civil programme has not benefited from, and indeed is not to some extent dependent upon, the military programme. Much of the research done for production of military materials is also useful for civil reactors; major plants built for military purposes, such as Calder Hall, are being used as prototypes for civil plant; factories built to make uranium and to extract plutonium for the military programme can be used for the civil programme, thus enabling costs to be spread over a large output at a time when civil demand is still small. Eventually civil nuclear power will undoubtedly stand on its own feet; in the meantime it has gained from the military programme in much the same way as civil aircraft development has gained from military interest in the aeroplane.

Such then is the brief history, and a glance into the future, of Calder Hall and gas-cooled reactors generally. Discussed at intervals ever since an atomic pile was first proposed, the gas-cooled natural-uranium reactor has had many ups and downs; it has been rejected in favour of water-cooled and air-cooled piles; it has been frowned on as wasteful of uranium and abused as big, clumsy, and out of date. Nevertheless designers have returned to it again and again, until finally a careful feasibility study showed clearly that it really was worth building; it would be safe and robust, it would not involve extravagant extrapolations of existing knowledge, it would give power sooner than any other type and at a reasonable price. So it has been built at Calder Hall, a source of power and of fuel with many possibilities for development in the future, an achievement of which Britain can be proud.